STEAMING ON

ENGINES & WAGONS FROM THE
GOLDEN AGE OF STEAM POWER

ERIC SAWFORD

SUTTON PUBLISHING

First published in 1998 by
Sutton Publishing Limited · Phoenix Mill
Thrupp · Stroud · Gloucestershire · GL5 2BU

British Library Cataloguing in Publication Data
A catalogue record for this book is available from the British Library.

ISBN 0-7509-1484-X

Title page photograph: Marshal no. 43560 *Winifred*, pictured at Great Wymondley in the 1960s.

A typical E class Aveling & Porter 10 ton roller at one of the Stamford rallies in the 1960s. Works no. 11647 was completed in October 1926 and was a single-cylinder 6 nhp design. Rollers such as this were a familiar sight on our highways well into the 1960s. Fortunately the preservation movement was well established by then and many were saved for preservation.

 ™ ALAN SUTTON™ and SUTTON™ are the
trade marks of Sutton Publishing Limited

Typeset in 10/12 pt Palatino.
Typesetting and origination by Sutton Publishing Limited.
Printed in Great Britain by Butler & Tanner, Frome, Somerset.

Contents

Unquestionably the most spectacular photograph I have taken to date, this picture shows road locomotives in action several years ago on hilly terrain at Stourpaine, Dorset. Leading is the 1909 Garrett road locomotive no. 27946 *Vera*, followed by the Burrell *Lord Roberts* and the well-known 1919 10 nhp McLaren no. 1652 *Boadicea*.

Frank Lythgoe's well-known engine collection includes a number of magnificent showmen's road locomotives. Here, one of the collection is hauling six others around the main ring – this display is always popular with the crowds. Unfortunately, due to the sheer length of this display they are seldom in a straight line. The Burrell 8 nhp no. 3093 *Dreadnought* makes a splendid sight as it hauls six others, the first three in the line being Burrell, Fowler and McLaren engines respectively.

Introduction

It is many years since the traction engine preservation movement started, the first engine events being held in the mid-1950s. There were, however, odd examples preserved by individuals before that date. Those who took part in events at that time could not possibly have imagined the present-day situation. Many owners and enginemen who took part in the early years were 'old hands' who had spent their working lives with these magnificent examples of steam power. Nowadays, engine owners come from a wide range of backgrounds, but most importantly, they all have an interest in steam.

During the 1950s there were still many abandoned engines to be seen around the British Isles, some having been neglected for a great many years. The lucky ones were under cover, many others were simply left where their fire had gone out for the last time. Such is the British climate that these engines, left unprotected, soon started to deteriorate. In due course rust and corrosion ate away steadily, the moving parts seized up and the engines came to the attention of scrap metal dealers, the brass and copper parts soon starting to disappear, especially from isolated examples.

Many engines were inspected around this time with a view to possible preservation, but those in need of expensive boiler and firebox repairs were rejected, the prospect of a new firebox or boiler barrel being regarded as completely out of the question. As for those which had become derelict over the years and were little more than rusty hulks, they were of interest but nobody was prepared to attempt to restore them. But since those distant days great advances in engineering techniques have made it possible for all parts to be manufactured. Gone are the days of cutting out wasted pieces and welding in new materials: new boiler barrels and fireboxes are now common.

Many readers may recall W.J. King's famous sale at Bishop's Lydeard in 1988 when a number of derelict Foden wagons were dragged out of the undergrowth and sold by auction. At around the same time two very early Fowler ploughing engines, known as the 'Inkbarrow' pair, were sold; these are now fully restored. In 1995, when the Philp collection went under the auctioneer's hammer, just about everybody involved in the preservation movement attended. Some of the engines were in a very advanced state of dereliction, especially two 4CD Garrett rollers, one of which broke in half when being moved, but all the engines were sold. The 'star of the show' was a Garrett traction engine which had enjoyed some degree of cover over the years, and this engine is currently being restored.

Even as late as the 1960s a number of steamrollers were still to be found at work, owned by contractors and local authorities; others were to be seen at the roadside or in contractors' yards. By this time the preservation movement was well under way and numerous examples of these rollers were rescued; and once owners realized there was a demand for what they had previously regarded as useless old equipment, littering up the yard, advertisements started to appear 'For sale by tender'. Despite this many rollers were purchased for what is by today's standards a very reasonable amount.

Unfortunately, the last remaining examples of some engine builders or of a particular company's design were cut up, especially in the late 1940s and early 1950s. The last remaining Brown & May traction engine was sadly lost in the 1960s. One company which had odd examples still intact until just before the preservation movement began was Fysons of Soham, but none of them has survived. Large dumps of engines were cleared and some readers may well recall the engines awaiting cutting up in the scrapyard near Cambridge station. Ploughing engines were still quite often to be seen lying derelict in the early 1960s: I can remember several in Cambridgeshire at that time, and happily most, if not all, have survived.

Over the years enthusiasts have started to look further afield, because most of the companies had thriving export markets. As a result quite a number of derelict engines and wagons have returned home. The dry climate of some countries helped to preserve many of those which became derelict; nevertheless, despite their often remote location, many of the parts were missing when the engines were rescued for preservation. Some of these may look a little strange to people accustomed to the standard designs for the British market. The Fowler type BAA and much more recently the Marshall light traction, which has a steam dome disc crank and friction clutch, are good example. These engines were supplied to burn wood and straw. For those more used to Fowler BB1 ploughing engines the appearance in steam of the first Z7 design came as a shock owing to its massive proportions. Some Z7 engines which returned from East Africa had worked on sugar estates and were in remarkably good condition. If it were not for wagons which have returned from overseas we would have no examples of Atkinson, Aveling & Porter and Foster designs with us today. And who knows, perhaps somewhere there are more examples of lost designs, waiting for an enthusiast to rescue them from oblivion.

The movement is certainly not one way: quite a number of examples which were a familiar sight at British rallies over the years have been sold to enthusiasts abroad. One example, a Sentinel wagon with tanker body frequently seen transporting water for

A trio of Burrell road locomotives quietly raise steam at the start of the day. From left to right, they are 5 nhp no. 3996 *Conqueror*, built in 1924, 5 nhp no. 3824 *Lord Fisher of Lambeth* of 1919, and 6 nhp no. 3593 *Duke of Kent*, completed in June 1914. The latter engine has been seen in many parts of the country and on the continent over the years.

Only rarely does one have the opportunity of photographing three Sentinels in a row without anyone obstructing the view. Nearest the camera is a fine example of the S4 design, no. 9016 built in 1934. The 'S' series was ahead of its time: these fast efficient wagons boasted electric lighting, pneumatic tyres, windscreen wipers and many other improvements over the earlier designs. Next is 'Super' no. 5256, built in 1924, and beyond it is another of this type, no. 6327, built in 1925. Between the 'Super' and 'S' series the company introduced the 'DG' design.

engines, is now in Australia. The Foden 'Colonial' wagon which returned from Australia and was restored to working order, in a bright yellow livery, by the late Tom Varley is now in Germany. Other engines and wagons are now owned by enthusiasts in many other countries, notably Holland, Sweden and the United States.

After so many years engines and wagons still make the headlines occasionally. For example, parts were discovered recently in old mine workings and high in the mountains at a stone quarry in the Lake District. And who would have thought a Sentinel wagon with tanker body and complete tar-spraying equipment would come on the market in 1997 at the well-known Chilford Hall sale. This was a wagon that many enthusiasts knew little or nothing about.

Many showmen's road locomotives ended their working days on agricultural work, often retaining the canopy but with the dynamo and twisted brasswork removed. As with other traction engines, many ended up derelict or in a scrapyard. A considerable number have been preserved although during the late 1950s and 1960s some of them were to be seen at events still largely as they were at the end of their working lives, albeit with mechanical problems rectified, cleaned and with a new coat of paint. These have long since been restored to their former glory.

Showmen's road locomotives are always eye-catching, their polished brasswork and gleaming paintwork highlighted by the coloured lights quietly driven by the engine's dynamo. Burrells of Thetford, was a leading company in the construction of this type of

Two Clayton & Shuttleworth traction engines with a Burrell showman's engine in the ring at Pickering. The nearest engine is 7 nhp single-cylinder no. 43187 *Agricola*, built in 1910, and next to it is another single-cylinder design, a 5 nhp, no. 38742 *Louise*, built in 1906. The Burrell, now preserved in North Yorkshire, is no. 3878 *Island Chief*, a 6 nhp engine built at Thetford in 1921; it spent much of its working life on the Isle of Wight, hence its name.

engine and has by far the largest number of survivors in preservation. The oldest, no. 1876 *Emperor* built in 1895, was only used on this work for a short time before returning to Thetford where it became the works crane engine for many years. *Emperor* has been restored to showmen's specification and can be seen at Hollycombe. Built three years later was no. 2072 *The Masterpiece*, which spent most of its working life in the Bristol area and still retains straked wheels.

There are several other types of Burrell showmen's road locomotives, of 5, 7, 8 and 10 nhp, including the 'Devonshires' which were designed for use in the west country and wherever narrow roads and limited access were encountered. At the other end of the scale are the magnificent 'Special Scenics', the ultimate Burrell design; twenty of these were built, of which eleven survive. These engines are equipped with two dynamos, the smaller of which was intended to excite separately the field coils of the main dynamo thus controlling the heavy demand of starting a scenic railway. Not all of the surviving Burrell showmen's engines are restored or in working order. There are, at the time of writing (1997), some which are nearing completion and will make a welcome return to the rally fields in the next few years.

Fowlers of Leeds were renowned for their heavy haulage engines, which used to perform many Herculean tasks, such as hauling huge difficult loads throughout the country. Fowlers also constructed showmen's engines, quite a number of which still survive, the oldest dating back to the late 1890s. The youngest survivor is no. 20223 *Supreme*, a 10 nhp 'Super Lion' B6 design built in 1934 for Welsh amusement caterer Mrs A. Deakin of Brecon. The last showman's engine built by the company, it was a special order with left-hand steering and chrome fittings in place of the more usual brass. This engine worked on the fairgrounds until the Second World War when it was commandeered by the government

Engines built by several companies in this picture taken at Pickering. Nearest the camera is Fowler 4 nhp 'Tiger' tractor no. 14406 *Mtoto*, built in 1917. Next in line are two Fowlers, an A4 class, no. 8424 built in 1899, and a B5 class, no. 9544 completed in 1903. Two other Fowler engines are at the end of the line, including an example of the distinctive class BAA. Several of these engines spent their working lives in Australia.

and used to haul new railway locomotives to the Glasgow docks. Like so many fine engines it ended up in a Surrey scrapyard from where it was rescued in the late 1950s.

Showmen's road locomotives built by other companies have also survived. These include several Fosters, a company highly regarded for their powerful designs. There are also a number of sole survivors: *General Buller*, built in 1912 by Brown & May Ltd of Devizes; the Foden *Prospector*, built in 1910; and the Garrett no. 27160 *British Hero*. The latter was not built as a showman's road locomotive but was converted to this role, working for a Wellingborough-based showman. After a great many years out of the public eye this engine reappeared with its new owners in 1997.

McLarens of Leeds were well known for their 10 nhp heavy haulage engines, quite a number being built for gun haulage in France during the First World War. One such was no. 1623 *Goliath*, which was later purchased by the well-known amusement caterer Pat Collins, who converted it to full showman's specification and used it in the Midlands.

There are a great many types of engine in preservation, built over a long period by a number of companies. This book contains illustrations of a very representative selection, but every year sees something new, and among the pictures here are examples taken in 1997. Portable engines are not included, important and interesting as they are, as this is a vast subject and deserves a title in its own right. The steam-engine movement has become very well established over the years, and each new season is eagerly awaited by owners, enthusiasts and general public alike. We are fortunate that so many steam enthusiasts are prepared to seek out, fully restore and maintain – often at considerable expense – these engines, which are such an important part of our engineering history. Long gone are many of the competitive events held at early rallies, the trend in recent years leaning towards theme events, perhaps based on a particular company's engines or

This is a rare sight: four Burrell crane engines together. This unusual picture was taken at the Weeting rally. From left to right they are 7 nhp no. 3197 *Old Tim*, built in 1910, 6 nhp no. 3829 *His Majesty*, built in 1920, 8 nhp no. 3695 *Lord Derby*, built in 1915, and last but not least, the youngest example, 5 nhp no. 4074 *The Lark*, built in 1927 and supplied to J. Reynolds of Bury St Edmunds, Suffolk. The crane and jib on *Lord Derby* were fitted in preservation and were taken from the former Burrell works engine *Emperor*.

those owned by a well-known steam operator. At Carrington in May 1997 the theme was engines which have returned to Britain after spending their working life overseas. This is a very refreshing approach as it allows people to concentrate on a particular aspect, and the different designs which evolved over the years can be more easily compared.

In 1996 Burrell no. 3130 came all the way from New Zealand to attend a rally. This 10 nhp traction engine was originally despatched to Reid & Gray of Dunedin on 29 July 1909. Initially it was used with a twenty-furrow plough, but in later years it worked on grain and timber haulage. In 1942 it came into the ownership of the Hawkins family who used it in their timber business until 1965, when it was restored by them and attended events in New Zealand. On 25 May 1996 the Burrell left New Zealand on the long journey home, arriving at Tilbury in early July. Within a short time it was in action at the Weeting rally where it naturally attracted much attention. It was seen at various rallies in both 1996 and 1997, but it is expected to go back to New Zealand eventually.

Wm Allchin Ltd
Globe Works, Northampton

This highly respected company was founded in 1847 but it was a number of years before they produced a portable steam engine. In due course the company went on to construct traction engines, road engines, rollers, wagons and many other designs before going into voluntary liquidation in 1931. Compared to some engine builders, Allchin's production of traction engines was not particularly high, 221 being constructed in all, commencing in 1872. Eventually the range consisted of single-cylinder and later double-crank compounds in 6, 7 and 8 nhp. Fortunately seventeen have survived in Britain and another one in Ireland; one of these survivors started life in 1931 as a road-roller. The last Allchin traction engine was completed in 1925 and one of the final examples, a 7 nhp single no. 3251 *Royal Chester*, is widely known in preservation. One 6 nhp compound, no. 1458, which was completed in June 1909, will be familiar to many readers as over the years it has travelled to countless rallies, especially in Dorset, Gloucestershire and Cheshire, from its base in Bedfordshire. There are examples of the company's 6, 7, and 8 nhp single-cylinder designs and also the 6 and 7 nhp compounds in preservation. Many of the traction engines went to new owners in neighbouring counties, while a few were exported through their agents Smellie & Co. of Brisbane, Australia, where at least one still survives.

Rather surprisingly, Allchin's did not become very involved with road locomotives, constructing only six. One of these, no. 1246, started life as a road engine in Derbyshire, but was returned to the works after a short time for conversion to showman's specification. Subsequently working for Fred Gray of Kensal Green, London, now bearing the name *Shamrock*, it did not remain with him for long before passing to a new owner. Another of the road engines was an 8 nhp 'Colonial' type which was sent out to Australia, where it still survives.

Despite constructing its first steamroller in 1893 (a convertible), the company did not have an active role in this market, building only fourteen examples. Two still survive, both of which are in the Northampton area in 1997. Both started their working life for Northampton Corporation, as nos 1 and 2 rollers respectively. The only other roller, no. 3858, was converted to a traction engine in preservation.

Allchin's did, however, become successful in the steam-wagon market, building in total 263, the first seven of which were 'undertypes', from 1906 onwards. This number exceeds the combined total of traction, road engines and rollers. Production switched to overtypes in 1913, and these included 3, 4, 5 and 6 ton models; among them were six six-wheeled articulated wagons but these proved to be less popular with the customers than the standard design. Among the companies operating fleets of Allchin's wagons were W.E. Chivers of Devizes, Hall & Co., and the Eastern Motor Wagon Co. Ltd based in North London. The range also included 'Colonial' models, fourteen of which went out to Australia. No example of an Allchin wagon has survived in the British Isles.

Allchin's publicity boasted its engines' efficiency, strength, economy and reliability. However, in comparison with other builders' wagons, their lower working pressure resulted in them being rather sluggish.

This 8 nhp single-cylinder Allchin traction engine, no. 1311 *Lena,* was completed in August 1905 and supplied to J. & E. Ison of Market Bosworth. It is currently preserved in Ireland but has returned to Britain on several occasions to attend events in various parts of the country. This picture was taken at the 1996 Allchin gathering at Northampton.

This is 7 nhp single-cylinder no. 1105 *Ellen*, completed at Northampton in August 1899 and supplied to Jas Coultas of Grantham, Lincolnshire. Pictured at Rempstone in 1963, this engine was at that time to be seen at many events in the Midlands. It is one of three surviving Allchins, all built in the 1890s.

For many years this Allchin 6 nhp Compound no. 1458 *Jane* was seen on the rally fields without a canopy. Completed in June 1909, it was supplied to H. & R. Cole of Ashbrook, Gloucestershire. Preserved in Bedfordshire, it is one of four surviving Allchin compounds. Over the years it has been seen at events in many parts of the country. This picture was taken at the 1996 Allchin gathering.

This fine example of Allchin's 7 nhp single-cylinder design was completed at the Northampton works in August 1922 and supplied to Story Bros of Barrowden, Rutland. The stovepipe chimney gives the engine a very different appearance. Seventeen traction engines built by Allchin's survive in Britain and Ireland, most of which are single-cylinder designs.

This 7 nhp Allchin traction engine was completed at the Globe Works in early November 1907 as works no. 1415, and was sold to James Hobden of Ringmer, Sussex. He was evidently impressed as he later purchased a second engine from Allchin's. Based on the Isle of Wight, *The Havenstreet Queen* is regularly to be seen at the Great Dorset Steam Fair.

There are two Allchin steamrollers in preservation, both of them single-cylinder engines. This is no. 1187, completed in November 1901. A 6 nhp design weighing 10 tons, it was sold new to Northampton Corporation, becoming their no. 2. The other surviving steamroller, no. 1131, another 10 ton design, was the Corporation's no. 1. Both are preserved in the Northampton area.

Sir W.G. Armstrong-Whitworth Ltd
The Openshaw Works, Manchester

This company is better known among steam enthusiasts for its railway locomotives, notably the LMS class 5 4–6–0s, 'Black Fives', but it did make a rather brief and belated incursion into the steamroller market. Seven examples have survived in the British Isles. Built between 1923 and 1926, these are all piston-valve compounds, six of them being 10 ton models and the seventh a 12 ton model. The range of rollers produced by the company consisted of 8, 10, 12 and 15 ton designs, and they were normally supplied in a standard finish of rich light umber picked out in chrome. Armstrong's paid particular attention to accessibility to all working parts on their rollers.

Armstrong's also had a quick reverse tandem type design for use on the asphalt and bituminous surfaces which were becoming more widely used at the time. All the rollers produced by Armstrong-Whitworth Ltd were built at the Openshaw works which covered 115 acres, and the company had many branches and agencies overseas.

This 10 ton Armstrong-Whitworth road-roller, no. 10R2, was completed in March 1923, and is the oldest of the surviving examples. It is seen here at the 1974 Expo Steam held at the East of England Showground, Alwalton, Peterborough. It was one of a fine selection of rollers assembled that year.

Works no. 10R22 *Stormer*, completed in September 1924, spent its working life on Ipswich docks.

Atkinson
Kendal Street, Preston

There are a number of single examples of early wagons preserved in Britain and only very rarely are they seen together. Some of them, such as this unique Atkinson, are in private hands, others are exhibits at the Commercial Vehicle Museum, Leyland. Atkinson's was established by two brothers and a friend in 1907 and traded as Atkinson & Co. from Kendal Street, Preston. The demand for wagons in the First World War resulted in their own designs being produced. The first design, a 6 ton design (no. 1) appeared in 1916, and testing took place in and around the works for several months. It was eventually sold to local owners and remained in service until the 1930s. In 1918 wagon production was moved to the company's Frenchwood Works, Preston; the Kendal Street site continued to be used for repairs and servicing steam vehicles. Over the following years Atkinson's constructed 4, 6 and 8 ton wagons as well as tractors, most of them being sold to owners in the Liverpool area. Development was ongoing and in 1923 an articulated tractor unit appeared, having a 12 ton capacity.

The company also developed an overseas market; indeed if they had not, there would be no Atkinsons left. 'Colonial' type no. 72 was built in 1918 and exported to Australia. It was rescued in 1971 and returned to this country five years later. It was extensively rebuilt as part of the Gisburn collection and changed hands again in 1984.

The company's financial position resulted in a merger with Walker Bros (Wigan) Ltd in the early 1920s and in 1925 the named changed to Atkinson Walker Wagons Ltd. New wagons and tractors were constructed, but times were difficult and the merger only lasted until 1930 when it was terminated. Although Atkinson's struggled on for a short time things did not improve and they went out of business. In 1933 a new company was formed, but its involvement with steam was short-lived.

Atkinson's built many 'Colonial' type steam-wagons for export, and the only example to be seen in the British Isles today is one of these, which spent its entire working life in Australia. Its early history is somewhat sketchy, but it is thought to have been supplied originally to the Swan Brewery in Perth, later working at a gold mine and ending up derelict in the bush near Wiluna where it stayed for almost thirty years. This splendid 6 ton example is thought to be no. 72, completed in 1918 and fitted with a Duplex Uniflow engine.

Aveling–Barford Ltd
Grantham, Lincs.

This company produced steamrollers from 1937 onwards for both the home and overseas markets. In preservation are examples of three classes: seven W class 6 nhp 10 ton engines, the earliest completed in October 1937; the much smaller R class 4 nhp 6 ton rollers represented by five built between 1937 and 1946; and the seven remaining T class 5 nhp 8 ton rollers built between 1947 and 1950. Some of these Aveling & Barford rollers had a very short working life, modern diesel-powered units with their easy starting and low maintenance requirements soon replacing them. One of the T class engines returned home from Sri Lanka in the early 1990s. The Aveling & Barford rollers are all single-cylinder, piston-valve two-speed designs.

The final T type design was an excellent engine incorporating a considerable number of improvements. The operating pressure was 200 psi, the piston-valves operated by Stephenson link motion. Enclosed steering worm and gear, crosshead driven-feed pumps, stayless type firebox requiring no roof stays and easier access to the footplate were just some of the many improvements. Nevertheless, they were unable to compete with the diesel rollers now becoming established, and compared with some of the early Aveling & Porter designs the working life of the Aveling–Barford engines was very short.

Aveling–Barford Ltd built steamrollers into the early 1950s, despite the increasing competition from diesel-powered units. The 4 nhp single-cylinder 6 ton roller, works no. AG758 *Gisela*, was completed in October 1946 and supplied to Cumberland County Council who used around Whitehaven. Sold in 1964 and purchased for preservation two years later, it is now at the Amberley Museum, Sussex.

There are nineteen Aveling–Barford rollers in preservation, one of which was originally exported but returned to this country for preservation. The surviving rollers are all single-cylinder models with piston-valves and are two-speed in 6, 8 and 10 ton designs. This is works no. AC605, a 10 ton model completed in July 1937.

Aveling & Porter Ltd
Rochester, Kent

Mention Aveling & Porter Ltd to any steam enthusiast and they will immediately think of steamrollers, although these were by no means the only type of steam engine built by this famous company whose products were so familiar both at home and abroad. Although many other companies were involved with steamrollers Aveling's was unquestionably the market leader and certainly the first to become widely involved with this type of engine.

Travelling the highways of the British Isles during the early 1960s you would be likely to find steamrollers still at work, including many Avelings. Rollers were the last type of steam power in regular use, often well into the 1960s, until the ever-increasing tide of diesel-powered rollers replaced them; their working life over, many rollers were left to their fate in contractors' and Council Highway yards or even dumped in isolated laybys. Fortunately by this time the steam-preservation movement was well established and a large number of rollers were saved and given a second lease of life. Steamrollers could be purchased, at what today seems a ridiculously low price. Realizing that the old disused rollers slowly rotting away in their yards had a value, several councils advertised their survivors for sale by sealed tender. Contractors were often pleased to see them go to a good home and for a reasonable price, in the process clearing valuable space. This all resulted in many fine rollers built by Aveling & Porter and other companies being with us today.

The company's history starts in the middle of the nineteenth century when Thomas Aveling started a small engineering company at Rochester, Kent, in 1850. Four years later Thomas designed his first engine which was constructed for him in 1859 by Clayton & Shuttleworth of Lincoln. A move to new works two years later gave Thomas the space he needed to get started with his own construction. Richard Porter became a partner in 1862, and the first examples under the Aveling & Porter name were exhibited at Battersea that same year. Even in those formative years their engines were being exported not just to Europe but also to Australia. Until 1867 production had consisted of agricultural, road and ploughing engines together with accompanying equipment. Following road-roller experiments in 1865 the first example of this type appeared in 1867, and was a rather different design to those with which we are familiar. This engine, weighing a hefty 30 tons, had driving wheels at the front and ship's wheel steering. The immense weight caused some problems, resulting in the design being reintroduced in due course as a 15 ton model. This successful design was available in 15, 20, 25 and 30 ton models. The 'Batho' type, as it was known, was used in Great Britain, the United States, India and France.

Steamroller designs continued to develop at an increasing rate over the following years, and in 1880 the conical rolls were replaced with parallel ones of a design familiar today. One example, a model R10 5 nhp single built in 1882, still survives, as do several others of this type built in the same decade. The first of the compound designs was produced in 1886. The very heavy rollers of previous years had tended to crush the road materials and in view of this a 15 ton maximum weight was introduced, although this was to rise by one ton after the end of the First World War. Convertible engines which could be used either as a roller or traction engine simply by changing the roll or wheels became available, the range at that time extending down to a neat 6 ton design. Shortly after the turn of the century the tandem two-wheeled roller was introduced especially for use on bitumen and hot surfaces where a quick reverse was required to prevent the roller sinking into the newly laid surface. These were available in five weights, ranging from 5 to 15 tons.

After the war, competition, the scarcity of skilled labour and the high cost of production led to the reorganization of the factory, principally to spread construction and control costs to cope with the high demand both at home and overseas. In 1920 a new range featured in the company's literature with 'something for everyone'. No fewer than ten designs, both single-cylinder and compounds, were available in a weight range of between 6 and 20 tons. These rollers incorporated many improvements, notably the replacing of the slide valves by the piston type. Large numbers of these engines have survived into preservation. In 1921 the vertical boiler model made its debut, replacing the earlier tandem design. These rapid-manoeuvring rollers, especially designed to work with bituminous and tarmacadam surfaces, were widely known as the 'coffee pot' design. Aveling's also produced a limited number of 'Shay drive' rollers, which were driven by a vertical twin-cylinder engine geared directly to the rear roller. One example survives. Production of steam designs, together with their motor rollers, continued until the late 1930s.

Throughout their long history steamrollers had been Aveling & Porter's principal products, for which the company became highly respected and known worldwide for the quality of their designs and workmanship. But the company also produced many other types of steam power, including steam tractors, agricultural and ploughing engines, road locomotives, crane engines and steam wagons. The oldest surviving traction engine is works no. 721 which was built in 1871 and is now in the care of the Science Museum, London. Production of ploughing engines could never be compared with the huge number built by Fowler's of Leeds, although 328 were completed before construction ceased in 1921. Two examples are to be seen at Thursford Steam Museum, nos 8890/1, both built in 1918. Aveling's exported ploughing engines to several countries and in 1993 one such returned from Africa, a model PC8 compound, no. 6547, built in 1908.

As a company Aveling's did not become very involved with showmen's engines, building just two especially for this purpose. However, some of their road locomotives also found themselves on the fairgrounds, one of these being works no. 4885 *Samson*, which was built in 1901 for the Admiralty at Chatham dockyard and was later used by Pat Collins.

Many steam-engine builders became involved with the production of steam wagons. Aveling's was a comparatively late starter with construction commencing in 1909, offering 3 and 5 ton designs which had many features in common with their other engines. In due course conventional, flat, box and tipping bodies also became available. Wagons were built by Aveling's for sixteen years, during which time they produced 292 examples, 40 of which were exported. Only one Aveling wagon survives in the British Isles: no. 9282, a model FGP 5 tonner built in 1922, was one of only five wagons exported to Australia. It was rescued in a very derelict state, shipped home and fully restored.

Aveling's also experimented with the production of tramway locomotives for use at industrial locations, attempts to get into the public tramway systems in the early years being largely unsuccessful. The tramway engines were very closely allied to traction engine designs, and some were little more than a traction fitted with, and running on, flanged wheels. With their short wheelbase, these were ideal for industrial sidings which often had tight, restricted curves. Two examples are fortunately still to be seen in working order: no. 8800 *Sir Vincent*, which was built in 1917 and spent most of its life at BOCM Oil Mills at Erith in Kent and other nearby sites, and no. 9449 *Blue Circle*, a 2–2–0 single-cylinder slide-valve engine which was built in 1926 and supplied new to Holborough Cement Works, Snodland, Kent. Both of these engines are preserved in Northamptonshire and on occasions make guest visits to preserved railways.

Aveling & Porter has the highest number of steam engines in preservation, closely followed by Fowler's of Leeds. The majority of the Aveling survivors are steamrollers although a considerable number of other designs have fortunately also survived.

This fine example of the Aveling & Porter 3 nhp single-cylinder A class tractor was completed at Rochester in March 1924. Tractors of this type were widely used for light haulage work, such as local deliveries of market produce, bricks and many other products.

Like so many of the principal engine-building companies, Aveling & Porter constructed tractors over a long period of time, producing several designs. This is an excellent example of the 4 nhp GND class compound weighing 5 tons. Works no. 9183 *The Pirate* was completed in August 1920 and this picture was taken at Manby rally in 1991.

Aveling & Porter works no. 8288 *Fire Queen*, an example of the 4 nhp compound GND class, was built in 1914 just before the outbreak of the First World War. It was purchased for preservation in 1961 from James Graven & Son of Ely by the late Tom Paisley, becoming part of his sizeable collection which was sold by auction in October 1980. It is pictured at the Chatteris rally, Cambridgeshire, in 1963.

This Aveling & Porter convertible traction engine always travels to and from events under its own steam, towing a van. Compound 6 nhp works no. 8679 is an example of the KLD class; it was completed in January 1916 and supplied new to the East Riding of Yorkshire County Council. It spent most of its working life in the Beverley area. Note the hinged smokebox door.

There are not many road locomotives built by Aveling & Porter in preservation. This example of the company's YLD design is a three-speed 6 nhp compound, works no. 8471 *Clyde*, completed at Rochester in December 1914. It was supplied new to S. Frampton of Farnham and was used on general haulage and army contract work during the First World War. In its later working life it was operated by other members of the Frampton family in Cornwall. It has had several owners during preservation.

This massive 8 nhp two-speed LC8 class Aveling & Porter road locomotive, works no. 4885 *Samson*, was completed in November 1901 for the Admiralty and used at Chatham dockyard. The Admiralty specification included two water columns and pressure gauges as well as a capstan fitted to the rear axle outside the rear wheel (long since removed). The engine later came into the ownership of G. Thurlow & Sons of Stowmarket and was then converted to showmen's specification for Charles Presland, remaining with him until 1946. Later it spent some time in use as an agricultural engine for a new owner before passing into preservation.

14

This FGP class 'Colonial' compound 5 ton tipping wagon, works no. 9282, was completed in January 1922 and exported to Australia. It was supplied new to Gudgegory Council near Sydney, and some years later it was sold to Mudgee Council, for which it worked until 1936. It was then sold to a gold-sluicing plant where it was used for several years before being laid aside, eventually becoming derelict. Discovered in 1978, it was crated, shipped home and completely restored in a matter of months.

This picture shows a PC8 class Aveling & Porter ploughing engine, works no. 6547, an 8 nhp compound built in 1908, at the 1993 Great Dorset Steam Fair, in the year that the engine returned home from West Africa. There are only two other Aveling ploughing engines in the British Isles, so once restoration of this engine is completed it is sure to attract considerable attention.

Looking at this picture of Aveling & Porter E class 10 ton roller no. 10114 *Cumberland*, it is difficult to believe it was entombed under a mound in a children's playground in London until 1990! The roller carries the name *Cumberland* after the former market-square near Euston station where it spent so many years in the dark. It is seen here at the 1996 Weeting rally.

This Aveling & Porter roller is known to millions of people via television as it is owned by steeplejack Fred Dibnah of Bolton. It has been in his ownership since 1968. Works no. 7632 *Betsy* is a class BH0 5 nhp single-cylinder 12 ton model which was completed at Rochester in February 1912 and supplied to Flintshire County Council, becoming their fleet no. 3. Here the splendidly restored roller is being put through its paces at Astle Park.

Over the years Aveling's introduced a number of different roller designs, and this example is thought to be the last surviving 8 ton model with the flywheel between the hornplates. Works no. 4877, it was completed in October 1901 and is a 4 nhp one-speed single-cylinder design. It was supplied new to Finchley District Council where it remained for just two years before being sold to W. Buncombe of Highbridge, Somerset. It had several owners after him, and was in a dismantled condition for twenty years. Now completely restored, it made its rally debut in 1992.

Only nine Aveling rollers were built to the 'Shay' design. This is the prototype and the sole survivor, class MLD 8 nhp 6 ton roller, works no. 7411. It is a tandem roller driven by a vertical twin-cylinder engine which is geared directly to the rear roll. Completed in June 1911, it was supplied to Fulham Borough Council and remained with them for sixteen years before being sold to W. Buncombe of Highbridge, from whom it was purchased for preservation, making its first rally appearance in 1988.

Another very interesting Aveling roller is this 4 nhp 6 ton tandem design which is believed to be the sole survivor of its type in the British Isles. Works no. 6530 was completed in May 1908 and supplied new to Luton Corporation. It is seen here at Expo Steam shortly after restoration in 1980, resplendent in green livery. It is now in the ownership of Luton Museum Service.

Babcock & Wilcox Ltd
Lincoln

When this company took over Clayton & Shuttleworth Ltd in 1924 they acquired five single-cylinder slide-valve steamrollers to which they fitted their own maker's plates. These five rollers, two 4 nhp 6 tonners and three 5 nhp 10 tonners, were all sold in 1926. Two of the 10 ton rollers, nos 95/4013 and 95/4014, were supplied to the well-known contractors W. Buncombe of Highbridge, Somerset, and were still in use until 1961.

The surviving rollers which carry Babcock & Wilcox maker's plates were built by Clayton & Shuttle-worth following their take-over in 1924. The survivors – two 4 nhp 6 ton and three 5 nhp 10 ton designs – are all single-cylinder slide-valve engines. This 5 nhp 10 ton roller, works no. 95/4013 *Brutus*, was sold in February 1926 to Buncombe's of Highbridge, Somerset, and was still in use in the early 1960s.

Brown & May Ltd
Devizes, Wiltshire

Although this company ceased steam production in 1913 they built a large number of engines, many of which were portables of various designs. Sadly, information on the products is somewhat sketchy as no records are known to exist. Brown & May built around fifty self-moving engines, including traction and tractor designs. They also ventured into the showman's market, building twelve examples, of which two were 6 nhps and the rest a smaller 5 nhp design.

One of the 6 nhp showman's engines has survived into preservation in Lincolnshire. This is no. 8742 *General Buller*, which was completed in September 1912. A compound slide-valve engine weighing 13.5 tons, this was the last showman's built by the company and was supplied new to J. Cooke of North Wales; it travelled with his set of galloping horses, and both engine and horses were later sold to Mellor Bros of Nottingham. In 1936 the engine was purchased by its present owners and spent the remainder of its working life of threshing work. After standing derelict for many years, this fine and very interesting engine was fully restored to showman's specification and since then it has been seen at many events throughout the country.

Sure to attract much attention will be the sole surviving Brown & May 5 ton tractor, no. 8130, which was completed in October 1909. This engine had been converted to a roller, but is being restored to its original form. This tractor had a long working life and still requires a new boiler barrel and firebox plus many other parts, in addition to new front wheels and front axle which went missing when it was converted into a roller. Work is progressing steadily and it is hoped that it will make its rally debut in 1999 – eighty-six years after the company that built it ceased to exist. One other example has survived in New Zealand.

Brown & May Ltd of Devizes, Wiltshire, constructed a range of steam engines including a number of showman's road locomotives. No. 8742 *General Buller* was completed in September 1912 and was the last of its type built by the company; it is also the only survivor. Just over a year later Brown & May closed down, their steam contracts passing to Robey & Co. of Lincoln. *General Buller* was supplied new to Cooks of North Wales, and worked with a set of gallopers; the engine later passed to Mellor Bros of Nottingham and in its final working years it was used for agricultural work including threshing. It was not until 1970 that this fine engine was restored, and since then it has been seen at events in many parts of the country.

Charles Burrell & Sons Ltd
St Nicholas Works, Thetford

Burrell's is unquestionably one of the best-known engine builders, with an excellent reputation and high standards of engineering, attention to detail and finish. The company produced a wide range of designs over a long period, and fortunately a considerable number of them have survived. Like so many of their competitors, the company built for both the home and overseas markets. One of the principal markets was the supply of showmen's road locomotives and they built a great many of these fine engines in a range of designs and power outputs. The oldest survivor is no. 1876 *Emperor*, a 10 nhp two-speed single-crank compound built in 1895 and supplied to C. Twigden of Lutterworth; however, the engine was soon returned to Burrell's where in 1906 it was fitted with a crane and became the works engine, remaining on these duties for over twenty years before passing into the hands of Mornment & Ray Ltd of East Harling, Norfolk, where the last years of its working life were spent on agricultural duties. *Emperor* has now been restored to showman's specifications and is part of the Hollycombe collection; it can usually be seen in steam at weekends.

Another showman's engine built before the turn of the century is no. 2072 *The Masterpiece*; completed in March 1898, this engine was sold new to John Cole, amusement caterer of Staple Hill, Bristol. This engine retains its straked wheels and is the oldest surviving double-crank compound showman's road locomotive. A number of these engines, built around the turn of the century, are still to be seen, many in working order while others, at the time of writing, are still undergoing restoration; two of the latter group are *Ephraim* and *Endurance*. The 8 nhp no. 2701 *Black Prince*, built in 1904, is on display at Bressingham Steam Museum, although it has not been steamed for a long time.

The 'Devonshire' type showman's road locomotives were especially popular with west of England showmen and others whose normal working area had narrow roads and limited access points. Two of these 5 nhps, which were probably the widest travelled of all the showmen's vehicles, were no. 3509 *Rajah* and no. 3669 *Nero*; both were in the ownership of Bostock & Wombell menagerie proprietors and travelled widely from their Glasgow base. Another engine of this type, widely known in the north of England during its working life, is no. 3555 *The Busy Bee*. Shortly after being completed in 1914 it was commandeered for war work and was to be seen at that time – with no twisted brass or dynamo – either at Elizah Charnley Town End Sawmills, Ulverston, or on timber work in the Windermere and Ambleside districts; it was returned to its owner at the cessation of hostilities.

There are many famous showmen's engines: they are far too numerous to mention here but one cannot omit the finest of the Burrell designs, the 'Special Scenic' type. Twenty of these were built, of which eleven survive. These engines had a platform behind the chimney which carried an auxiliary dynamo; this was to excite the field coils of the main dynamo, thus providing a means of controlling the current, especially when starting heavy rides. The famous Burrell 'Gold Medal' tractors also found favour with showmen as they proved ideal for handling lighter loads. Some were supplied new to showmen, others after war service or after use on general haulage. In the early years of the twentieth century there was a considerable demand for tractors for a wide variety of haulage duties and many of these 5 ton examples spent their entire working lives on such duties.

Burrell's entered the ploughing engine market early. Together with Aveling & Porter and McLarens, they were competing against the market leaders in this field, Fowler' of Leeds. A pair of 8 nhp single-cylinder engines built at Thetford in 1879 have survived despite spending many years in a scrapyard where the ravages of time and weather took their toll. The two engines, nos 776 and 777, were supplied new to J.P. Wilberforce of Woolavington, West Sussex, where they remained until the early 1890s when they returned to Burrell's works. They were sold on in 1893 to E.W. Dorkin of Colchester, Essex, and eleven years later they were sold at auction to A. Borley, also in Essex, where they remained until 1917 when they were sold to the well-known engine dealers George Thurlow & Sons, Stowmarket. In due course the pair were on the move again, this time to Brize Norton, Oxfordshire. After a further few years' service they were sold for scrap to R. Edwards of Swindon; dumped there, as with so many engines throughout the country, they were left to slowly rust away, in time almost disappearing under a mass of undergrowth.

As might be imagined, after thirty-odd years the chance of them ever steaming again looked very remote. Fortunately the late Mr Paisley was on the lookout for interesting engines and he bought them, moving them to Manor Farm, Holywell, Huntingdonshire (as it was in those days). Work commenced on a major rebuild, involving new boiler, firebox, smokebox and countless other parts, and by 1980 one of the engines was taking shape. At Mr Paisley's untimely death the second engine had been stripped down and a certain amount of work started. The October sale saw both engines purchased by the late Tom Varley and the first, no. 777, soon made its appearance in steam. These two grand engines are now with the Museum of East Anglian Life in Stowmarket, and both are regularly to be seen in action during the summer months. Long may they continue to do so, as they are the only surviving Burrell ploughing engines.

Burrell's also entered the wagon market, but it was not until 1908 that work commenced in earnest on an 'overtype' project, although some work had been done on an undertype design some years previously. Some people are convinced that an undertype wagon was actually built, although there seems to be no evidence for this. Fodens had already taken a considerable lead in the market-place when the first Burrell, a 5 tonner, was ready. In due course a 6 ton design was introduced but this did not compare very favourably with the Foden design and consequently only a small number were built. No complete Burrell wagon has survived in the British Isles although parts of no. 4008, a 5 tonner built in 1925, do survive; this wagon was supplied new to H. Kay of Horsham, Sussex, and ran on solid rubber tyres.

In contrast, a fine selection of Burrell road locomotives have survived into preservation. These range from the 5 nhp designs to the powerful contractor's engine no. 3057 *Lord Roberts*, which in its working days hauled a variety of heavy loads, such as timber, bricks and boilers. One example which has been on the rally scene for many years is the splendidly restored 6 nhp *The Dalesman*, built in 1912 as works no. 3395 and supplied new to J. Hancock & Sons of Exeter who used it for brick haulage. Many years later, in the 1950s, while in preservation at Uttoxeter, it was named *City of Exeter*, receiving its present name when it changed hands in the mid-1960s.

The Burrell 6 nhp double-crank compound crane locomotive no. 3829 left St Nicholas Works on 15 March 1920 on its way to its new owners, T. & W.J. Hooper Contractors of Liskeard, Cornwall, although no jib was supplied. In October of the same year the engine was purchased by J. Hickey & Sons and moved to their Richmond Works; by this time it had received a crane jib and was named *His Majesty*, and it became well known in the London area working with and without the jib fitted. In the early 1960s, while still in that company's ownership, the engine took part in a few rallies in East Anglia. It was purchased by its present owners in 1964.

Another magnificent Burrell crane engine is the 7 nhp no. 3197 *Old Tim*, which was built in 1910 and supplied new to Screen Brothers of Oldbury, Birmingham, where it continued to work until 1958. This was certainly not a case of an engine being in use occasionally: during the First World War *Old Tim* regularly worked twenty-four hours a day, manned by two crews. What is even more remarkable is that in the 1990s this Burrell is still in its original livery. But nothing lasts forever and *Old Tim* will eventually have to be repainted. There is something particularly fascinating about crane engines. Much younger than *Old Tim* is no. 4074 *The Lark*, a 5 nhp model built in 1927 and supplied to J. Reynolds of Bury St Edmunds. Finished in Lake/Red livery, it was one of Burrell's last road locomotives.

None of the major engine builders could ignore the road-roller market with its large sales potential both at home and overseas. The rollers produced by Burrell's were of traditional design in a number of sizes and were sold to both home and overseas buyers. Almost forty Burrell rollers have survived into preservation.

Last, but by no means least, are the traction engines which comprised a major part of Burrell's entire works construction. As Thetford is situated in one of the major agricultural counties, a considerable number were sold to owners in eastern England. Others went to owners elsewhere in the British Isles and overseas, with New Zealand and Australia being particularly good markets. Several early traction engines have survived. The oldest is *Century*, built in 1877 and preserved just a few miles from its birthplace. This 8 nhp single-cylinder engine has been seen at a great many events throughout the country; for years it appeared in dark red livery but has recently been repainted green. Five engines, all singles built in the 1880s, have survived and there are even more from the 1890s, with numerous examples from the wide range of engines constructed right up to 1932. One of the highlights in 1996 was the return of no. 3130, a 10 nhp traction engine built in 1909 and exported to New Zealand. This massive engine spent much of its early working life on direct ploughing with a twenty furrow plough and in more recent years on haulage of grain and timber. It is in preservation in New Zealand and is often to be seen at rallies there. After a short visit to Britain it is expected to return to New Zealand.

On 1 July 1928 a public announcement was made to the effect that the Burrell range of products would be concentrated at Garrett's of Leiston, to whom all orders and enquiries should henceforth be sent. The final Burrell engines were built by this company, and one of these was the last showman's road locomotive, no. 4092 *Simplicity*, an 8 nhp engine supplied to Mrs A. Deakin of Brynmawr; interestingly, the engine's works plates recorded Charles Burrell & Sons Ltd as the builders. As with many showmen's engines, *Simplicity* was to finish its working life on general haulage in the Glasgow area. Sadly, despite being the last of a long line of showmen's engines built by Burrell's, it has not survived into preservation. The last two Burrells, nos 4093/4, built after *Simplicity*, were completed by what had once been a rival company.

Burrell's oldest surviving engine in the British Isles is 8 nhp single traction no. 748 *Century*, completed in October 1877. This veteran has been a feature at the Weeting rallies for many years, originally in dark maroon livery and more recently in dark green. It has also been seen at many other events throughout the country. There are no other tractions surviving from the 1870s, although there are five from the 1880s and several others constructed before the turn of the century.

Another Burrell traction engine, this is works no. 2159, completed in March 1899, a 7 nhp single-cylinder engine. A feature of the Weeting rallies is engines in action driving equipment as they would have done in their working days. The Burrell was all ready to provide power; note the set of 'spuds' in front of the rear wheels. The 'spuds' were fitted to the rear wheels in wet, sticky conditions.

Heavy ground conditions do not deter Burrell no. 3794 *Defiant* from moving around. Built as a traction engine in January 1919 but since converted into a road locomotive, this example of the 6 nhp double-crank design was supplied new to T. Stenner of South Moulton, Devon.

Lady Burrell is a fine example of the single-crank compound design. This 6 nhp single-cylinder traction engine, works no. 2147, was completed in Thetford in November 1898. *Lady Burrell* is one of sixteen traction engines built by the company in the 1890s and currently in preservation in the British Isles.

This magnificently restored Burrell traction engine is no. 3121 *Keeling*, an 8 nhp single-cylinder design completed in July 1909 and supplied to John White & Sons of Rettendon, Essex. The engine has since been fitted with belly tanks. It is seen here arriving on the Banbury rally field.

The splendid Woburn rallies of the 1960s will be well remembered by many enthusiasts. This picture was taken at the 1965 event and the engine is no. 4055 *Crimson Lady*, a 5 nhp compound built in 1927 and supplied to I. Sheldrake of Bunwell, Norfolk. It has been with the same owner for many years, taking part in numerous events.

One of the high spots of 1996 was the return to Britain of this large 10 nhp Burrell traction engine, works no. 3130, all the way from New Zealand. It was brought over by its owner to attend a few events and to return under its own steam to its birthplace in Thetford, where this picture was taken in July 1996. Built in 1909, the Burrell was dispatched to Reid & Grey of Dunedin, New Zealand; it was used initially on direct ploughing with a 20-furrow plough and later on hauling grain and timber. Note the long boiler, belly tanks, lengthy steam pipe and headlamp. This powerful engine is expected to go back to New Zealand eventually.

This is Burrell no. 3984, pictured at Haddenham; it is a typical example of the company's 7 nhp single-cylinder design. The engine was completed in June 1924 and dispatched to John Morgan & Sons of Barlow in Derbyshire.

Burrell's was also involved in the steamroller market as were most of the principal engine builders. Works no. 3994 *The Leader*, completed in November 1924, is a typical example of the 5 nhp compound 8 ton design. It did not have far to travel to its first owners, Doran Brothers of Thetford.

Only one pair of Burrell ploughing engines survive in the British Isles. No. 777, an 8 nhp single-cylinder design, was completed with its sister engine no. 776 in June 1879, and the pair were sold to R.W. Wilberforce of Lavington, Sussex. The engines passed through several hands, ending up very derelict in a Swindon scrapyard from where they were rescued by the late Tom Paisley. Work began on restoration, but neither was anything like finished when sold at auction to the late Tom Varley who completed the restoration. They are now at the Museum of East Anglian Life, Stowmarket, where they can be seen in action during the summer months.

One engine that became very well known during its working life in London was Burrell road locomotive no. 3829 *His Majesty*. This 6 nhp engine was completed in March 1920 and supplied to its first owner as a crane engine but without the crane jib. After a few months it passed into the hands of J. Hickey & Sons Ltd, who used it on heavy haulage in the London area and then as a works crane engine until 1950. After a period out of use it was restored to its former glory, and still in the company's ownership it attended a few rallies in the 1960s (but without the crane jib).

This is *Emperor* at Hinchingbrooke Park, Huntingdon, more than thirty years ago. This 10 nhp single-crank compound, works no. 1876, was completed in August 1895 as a showman's road locomotive for C. Twigden of Lutterworth. Although fitted with a dynamo platform and short awning, it did not carry showman's decorations. After a short time it returned to Burrell's works where it was fitted with a crane and took over the duties of the works engine. The engine later passed into the ownership of Mornement & Ray Ltd and was used on fen drainage work, and its last owner before preservation was Mr R. Palmer of Stoke Ferry. The engine is now back in showman's specification at Hollycombe Park.

Despite this Burrell crane engine's extremely hard working life, it has retained its original livery. Built in 1910, *Old Tim*, works no. 3197, was supplied new to Screen Brothers of Oldbury, Birmingham. Just a few years later the First World War broke out, and the resulting pressure on the works meant *Old Tim* was used for twenty-four hours a day with double manning. The engine was still in use until 1958 when it went into well-earned preservation. Over the years since, it has had several owners. The engine is currently undergoing overhaul, and its age almost certainly means that it will require a repaint at some point, which will leave just a few examples of engines still in their original livery.

Burrell 7 nhp road locomotive no. 3257 *Clinker* was completed on 11 January 1911 and supplied new to the Wingham Agricultural Implement Co. Ltd, Wingham, Kent who used it until the early 1920s when it passed to Mornement & Ray of East Harling, Norfolk. *Clinker*'s final work was fen drainage. The Burrell has since undergone a complete overhaul and is now to be seen at many events, travelling to and fro under its own steam.

In the early years of the preservation movement several fine showman's engines could be seen in action in road locomotive form. One such example is Burrell no. 3118 *Dreadnought*, pictured here at Ickleton in 1961. A 7 nhp engine, it was completed on 2 July 1909 as a road locomotive and supplied to McCreath & Co., Berwick on Tweed, where it was used on general haulage work. Seven years later it passed into showland service in the ownership of Wm Cross of Workington, and was later sold to C. Abbott of Norwich, who used it to haul and provide power for a Cakewalk and set of Chair o' planes. In 1940 it was sold again, this time out of showland. It has long since been fully restored to showman's specification and is seen at rallies throughout the year.

These magnificent Burrell road locomotives, photographed at Roxton, were all built at Thetford within a six-year period. Nearest the camera is no. 3395 *The Dalesman*, a 6 nhp engine of 1912; in the centre is the 7 nhp no. 3057 *Lord Roberts*, a contractor's engine more heavily constructed than normal; and on the right is 6 nhp no. 3593 *Duke of Kent*. They are a splendid sight, gleaming in the early autumn sunshine.

The Burrell 7 nhp road locomotive no. 3633 *Lord Kitchener* was built in 1914 and supplied new to W.E. Chivers & Sons, Devizes, Wiltshire. This company evidently liked Burrell's engines as over the years they purchased several other road locomotives and wagons.

This is the oldest original showman's road locomotive to survive into preservation and it is still on straked wheels. Works no. 2072 *The Masterpiece* was completed in March 1898 and supplied to John Cole, amusement caterer of Bristol, later passing into the ownership of Hardiman & Strong, also based in Bristol, and travelling with a set of three-abreast gallopers. This splendid 8 nhp engine was purchased for preservation in 1955, since when it has had several owners.

This superbly restored Burrell showman's road locomotive is only very occasionally seen in Britain as it is preserved in Melkweg, Holland. This picture was taken during one of its rare visits to the Great Dorset Steam Fair. Works no. 3926, a 5 nhp design, was completed on 30 March 1922 and sold to Henry Thurston of Northampton; here, under the name *Margaret*, it was used to work a set of chair o' planes, later helping with the all-electric drive Scenic Railway and also with a new Noah's Ark speedway. The engine now also carries the name *Stokomolief*.

This splendid Burrell showman's road locomotive was originally supplied new as a road engine to W.J. Taylor & Son Ltd of Midsomer Norton, Somerset. In due course it was sold to Mrs F. Symonds of Gloucester and converted to showman's specification, carrying the name *Earl Haig*. The engine is a 6 nhp design, works no. 3979. As with so many other showmen's locomotives, its final years were spent on agricultural work. Eventually being laid aside it slowly sank into the ground near Ely, Cambridgeshire, from where it was rescued and restored by its present owner.

This 8 nhp Scenic-type Burrell showman's road locomotive was supplied new to the well-known showman Pat Collins of Walsall. Completed in November 1920 as works no. 3865, it became known simply as *No. 1*, carrying plates to that effect. For a number of years it was on display at Thursford Museum but it has now moved to Lincolnshire. This picture was taken at the 1996 Carrington rally.

Pictured against a typical showground setting, this is the 7 nhp Burrell *Princess Royal*, works no. 2879, built in 1907. This engine was originally supplied to Henry Thurston & Sons, Cambridge, carrying the name *Lord Nelson*. In 1933 it passed into the ownership of Fred Harris & Sons of Ashington, Sussex, where it was named *Sweet Nothing* and eventually *Princess Royal*. The engine eventually finished up in Hardwick's scrapyard at West Ewell from where it was purchased for preservation in 1957. It has had several owners since then.

Many showmen's road locomotives changed their names during their working life. Burrell 6 nhp no. 3878 was one of these. Completed in February 1921, it was supplied to Robert Payne of Beverley, Yorkshire, carrying the name *Excelsior*. It later passed into the ownership of Arnold Brothers of Cowes, Isle of Wight, becoming *Island Chief*. This engine has had several owners in preservation: during the early 1960s it was in North Norfolk, after which it was left in a dismantled state for some time, but it is now to be found back in Yorkshire.

This 8 nhp engine, no. 2789 *The President*, was built in 1905 as a showman's locomotive for G.H. Kemp of Leicester. It was converted for heavy haulage before the First World War and has been a static exhibit at the Bressingham Steam Museum for many years. Notice the large rear wheels and other embellishments. This photograph was taken at the Ickleton rally in 1961.

This Burrell showman's road locomotive has several times made the long journey south from its base at Aberdeen to take part in the Pickering rally. Works no. 3871 *Teresa*, a 7 nhp engine, was completed on 18 March 1921 and sold new to Sidney Stock of Ipswich. It later passed into the ownership of Hardiman & Strong of Bristol where it became *Pioneer*, and then on to John Cole of Bristol, becoming *Western Pioneer*. During preservation it was for some time on display at the Bygone Village, Fleggburgh, Norfolk, before moving north to its present owner.

This is Burrell 'Scenic' no. 3610 *William V* moving slowly across the field at Stamford rally in 1965. The engine was at that time in preservation in Bedfordshire. It was completed at Thetford on 31 August 1914 for Wm Murphy of Newcastle upon Tyne, providing power for his Scenic Motors, and was to have two more showland owners in the north of England before going on to J. Bottom & Sons of Green St Green, Kent. More recently, in preservation, it has been based at Falkirk carrying the name *Flower of Scotland*. Note the bracket for the auxiliary dynamo behind the chimney, although it was not fitted.

Burrell's of Thetford's finest showman engine design was the 8 nhp 'Special Scenic'. This is no. 3912 *Dragon*. This engine was completed in June 1921 and supplied to Anderton & Rowland, well-known west country showmen, and it became one of the best-known engines in that area. It later passed to Sam Smart & Sons of Bristol. This fine engine has been in preservation near Peterborough for many years and appears at events over a very wide area, travelling under its own steam to local shows.

Another Burrell showman's road locomotive to have had several names in its working days is the 8 nhp no. 4030 *Dolphin*, built in 1925. The engine's first owner was Wm S. Davies of Stoke on Trent; it was later sold to J. Shaw of Sheffield where it became *The Guv'nor* and then to H.J. Wallis of Seaforth, Lancs., where its name changed again, becoming *The Commando*. The engine was purchased for preservation in 1959 and is now part of the Frank Lythgoe collection.

The heavy electric scenic railway rides resulted in the development of the 'Special Scenic' road locomotives. These powerful engines could haul up to 40 tons in as many as eight trailers, a feat requiring considerable skill from both driver and steersman. The smaller dynamo behind the chimney excited the field coils of the main unit, providing a means of controlling the current variations when starting and accelerating the ride. These engines were also fitted with a jib crane to unload and assist assembling the ride. Works no. 3886 *Lord Lascelles* , built in 1921, was supplied new to Fred Gray of Hampstead Heath, the engine working until the outbreak of the Second World War, after which it spent twelve years laid up before being rescued for preservation.

Another 8 nhp 'Special Scenic', this is works no. 3909, completed on 20 April 1922 for A. Holland of Swadlincote, Derbyshire, where it was known as *Pride of the Road*. Renamed *Winston Churchill* during preservation, the engine is seen here taking part in the Grand Parade at Pickering, North Yorkshire, one of the best events at which to see showmen's road locomotives in the north of England.

This Burrell 'Gold Medal' tractor, no. 3631, was completed in late 1914 and exhibited at the Smithfield show in early December. It was sold to W. Gritt of Romsey carrying the name *Pride of Romsey*. In 1933 it passed into the ownership of Maurice Stokes of Basingstoke who converted it to a showman's type and used it to haul and power a set of Chair o' planes. The engine then carried the name *Bluebird*. It was purchased in 1959 for preservation and renamed once again, this time becoming *Kathleen*.

Burrell Gold Medal tractor no. 3452 *The May* is still in showland ownership, and travels to many events where it stands beside the owner's steam-powered galloping horses. Built in 1913, the engine was sold to W. Sedgwick of Oldham for use with his menagerie and hauling their *American Jungle*. It was purchased by its present owner in the early 1950s, and after a period in store it reappeared in the early 1970s.

Burrell no. 4062 *Lorna Doone* started life in 1927 as an 8 ton roller, being supplied new, complete with scarifier, to W.J. King of Bishops Lydeard, Somerset. The engine has since been converted to a 4 nhp compound tractor and it is seen here at Pickering rally in 1996.

Clayton & Shuttleworth Ltd
Stamp End Works, Lincoln

Clayton & Shuttleworth Ltd was one of a number of large engine building companies situated in the northern part of Lincolnshire. In their heyday the company's works covered 40 acres and employed over two thousand men. The company built a wide range of engines although they are best known for their traction engines and road-rollers, of which a considerable number have survived into preservation. Traction engines of both single-cylinder and compound designs were made. In 1923 the company offered the following:

	5 nhp	8 nhp	10 nhp
single-cylinder	£460	£545	£620
compound	£510	£625	£720

Road locomotives of 8 and 10 nhp were advertised for £725 and £825 respectively although only a few were built. The oldest example of the company's traction engines surviving in the British Isles is no. 32900, a 6 nhp single completed in December 1899 and supplied new to G. Harris of Ropley, Hants. Just eight years later it moved to a new owner, J. Potter of Coggeshall, Essex, where it remained for thirty-nine years before passing to its last commercial owner at Bulmer. The engine was purchased in 1957 but it was to be twenty years before restoration from its derelict state commenced. Just three years later it was in steam again, restored to its original livery, and is still a regular sight at events in eastern England.

None of the engine builders could afford to ignore the tractor market, and those built by Clayton's were known as the 'Little Hercules'. Clayton's came relatively late into this lucrative market, and although their product was good it never became a major threat to those builders who were already established in the market, such as Burrell's whose 'Gold Medal' tractor was one of the market leaders, and Garrett's, another East Anglian company achieving considerable sales with their popular 4CD design.

Only one example of a Clayton tractor is thought to survive. No. 49008 was completed in January 1920 and was the last tractor built by the company. At this time the market was still flooded with tractors, wagons and other equipment being sold by the War Stores Disposal Board following the end of the First World War. Their condition varied from well worn to almost new, but the sheer numbers of them depressed home sales for a considerable time. Orders for new tractors for the home market had been severely restricted, largely because of Government requisitioning, but several companies enjoyed the opportunity to fulfil outstanding orders. The surviving Clayton tractor was to become the works engine, serving in this capacity for many years, but in January 1934 it was sold and ended up in Radnorshire. It was later taken to East Anglia where it became a familiar sight on the rally fields.

Clayton & Shuttleworth was well known its 'overtype' wagons, for both home and overseas markets. The range included 3, 5, 6 and 7 tonners with some built as 'Colonials'. At the outbreak of the First World War most of their production was for the government, with over 300 wagons seeing service with the army in France. In the mid-1920s wagon production passed to another company, Clayton Wagons Ltd, whose Titanic Works in Lincoln were situated alongside the Great Northern Railway line. By this time the internal combustion engine lorry had proved itself, presenting a very serious threat to steam wagon construction. Despite this, various improvements were made and an 'undertype' design developed but this met with limited success. The undertype wagon was competing with the Sentinel DG series, of which, sadly, there are no survivors of the undertype design. Only a handful of Clayton & Shuttleworth wagons are in preservation in the United Kingdom, plus another one built in 1929 by Clayton Wagons Ltd.

The company built a great many portable engines over the years, of which eleven are now to be found in the British Isles. The steamrollers built by Clayton's were, in the early days, modified traction engines and, having realized this expanding market's potential, the company produced a neat design in the 1920s and sales started to increase. The knock-on effect of the war and non-payment for export sales soon caused serious problems, and in 1924 the well-known engineering company Babcock & Wilcox absorbed the engineering side of Clayton's, taking over the last batch of wagons. Other company products were taken over by Marshall's of Gainsborough. One Clayton roller, no. 48971, a 20 ton 'single' built in 1925, was to be seen in a layby at Llangymog near Bala in North Wales in June 1968, its canopy lettered J.E. Corfields Contractors, Abermule, Mont. The roller was in working order and was complete with plates and must have been one of the last rollers in commercial use. Fortunately it was rescued for preservation.

The oldest surviving Clayton & Shuttleworth traction engine in the British Isles is no. 32900, a 6 nhp single-cylinder completed in December 1899 and supplied new to G. Harris of Ropley, Hants. During its working life it had two other owners and was then purchased in 1957 in a derelict state, becoming part of the Philp collection. It is seen here restored to its original livery at its home base in Essex.

This 7 nhp single-cylinder Clayton & Shuttleworth traction engine, works no. 44103 *Enterprise*, built in 1911, was photographed in 1965 in the attractive surroundings of Woburn Park.

Clayton & Shuttleworth, one of the largest engine building companies based in north Lincolnshire, was particularly well known for its traction and wagon designs. This is works no. 39400, a 6 nhp 'single' built in 1907 and photographed at Weeting rally. It spent most of its working life with Fords of Mildenhall, Suffolk, and was restored in 1981.

This is the only known surviving example of the Clayton & Shuttleworth 4 nhp compound 5 ton tractor. Works no. 49008 *Apollo* was completed in January 1920 and was used as the works engine, only being sold on fourteen years later. Discovered in Radnorshire, it was purchased for preservation and during the early 1980s it was often to be seen at Weeting rallies.

This Clayton & Shuttleworth 5 ton wagon, works no. 48510 *Fenland Princess*, built in 1920, spent much of its working life with Southern Tar Roads and later with Northern Tar Roads being used as a tar sprayer. Like so many engines and wagons, it ended up at Hardwick's Scrapyard at Ewell in a very derelict condition with numerous parts missing and still with a tanker body.

Very few Clayton wagons have survived, although the company produced a number of designs, 3 and 5 ton for the home market and 6 and 7 ton 'Colonial' models. In addition, over 300 were supplied to the War Department for war service in France. Works no. 48347 is a fine example of the 5 ton design, built in 1919 and preserved in Lincolnshire.

This 10 ton single-cylinder Clayton & Shuttleworth steamroller, no. 48971 of 1925, was photographed at Llangymog, near Bala, North Wales, in June 1968. Owned by Corfields of Abermule, Monmouthshire, it was still in use and, as can be seen, is complete with all its plates. Happily the roller was rescued for preservation and it is currently based in Nottinghamshire under the name *Lady Jane*.

Davey Paxman & Co. Ltd
Standard Ironworks, Colchester

This was another highly respected East Anglian engine building company but only a small number of its traction engines have survived. All are single-cylinder, slide-valve designs, including a 6 nhp, three 7 nhp and 10 nhp straw-burning model constructed in 1908. There are in addition a number of portable engines in preservation. The company was particularly well known for the production of many types of stationary and portable engines used for many different applications. In addition to the general purpose tractions, the company catalogue also listed improved compound road locomotives and 3-shaft tractors. Among the special features of engines built by this company the catalogue boasted silent working, excellent fuel economy and increased power owing to higher working pressure.

Davey Paxman also had a thriving export business, especially with its 'Colonial' traction engines which were supplied to Argentina and other countries. Who knows, perhaps one of these may still exist in some isolated country district, waiting to be rescued from dereliction.

This Davey Paxman no. 13073 *Victoria* is the oldest survivor in the British Isles of traction engines built by this Colchester-based company. It was completed in July 1907 as a 7 nhp single-cylinder slide-valve engine. During its long working life it had several owners, among them Hertfordshire County Council. It was purchased by the late Tom Paisley in 1961, and just five years later it took part in the 1966 Davey Paxman Centenary celebrations; this photograph of it was taken not long after. In 1980 it was included in the engine sale held at Holywell.

Of the five surviving engines built by Davey Paxman, only one is a 6 nhp, the others being three 7 nhp and one 8 nhp designs. All are single-cylinder slide-valve engines. No. 16849 *Little Audrey* was completed in May 1911 and is the sole surviving 6 nhp in the British Isles. This is *Little Audrey* in action at Astle Park in 1995.

Fodens Ltd
Elworth Works, Sandbach, Cheshire

Nearly all the major engine building companies are associated with a particular design and with Fodens it is unquestionably the famous range of 'overtype' wagons. This very highly respected company also produced road engines, tractors and traction designs, starting with the latter in 1880. From the outset Fodens had standards of quality and durability which were second to none and the company quickly built up a high reputation.

The most famous model, the overtype wagon, the 5 tonner led the field, quickly becoming established in the market-place both at home and abroad. These wagons had the engine mounted on top of the locomotive type boiler and a heavy chain drive to the rear axle. It is hardly surprising that at the onset of the First World War the government commandeered the whole output, with the works at maximum production; as soon as the wagons were ready they were loaded on to railway wagons, whole train loads leaving Sandbach on their way to the British Army in France. After the cessation of hostilities many were to return and were eventually offered for sale, flooding the market. Some had been damaged and did not return while others, such as no. 7768, passed into the hands of French owners and spent their working lives in France. This particular wagon was eventually returned to Britain, albeit a great many years later; restored in WD livery, it is a very fitting tribute to those who worked with the wagons during the war and to the wagons themselves.

The company introduced its 6 ton C type wagon design in the early 1920s. These wagons had many new developments, principally intended to improve operation on the road. Ackerman-type steering, improved lubrication that required less maintenance on the road, higher boiler pressure and – sure to be welcomed by the crews – an improved cab. The company also developed an undertype design, known as the 'Speed Series', in 1926 but it was never likely to replace the overtypes. One of them, no. 13750, built in 1930, has survived, and was among the Fodens which were sold at the famous W.J. King sale on 14 May 1988 when several very derelict wagons and three traction engines were auctioned. The 'Speed Six' was in a very poor condition and its restoration will be a very lengthy and expensive project; however, when finished it will attract much attention.

Fodens also looked into the steam bus market and some were built although they were never very common. Possibly the best known was the example used to transport the Fodens Motor Works band to engagements. No. 11340 is a replica of this vehicle.

The tractors built by Fodens were employed on very different types of work ranging from straightforward haulage to timber handling. The 'Sun tractor', also known as the 'M' type, with round stayless firebox, was a late design and only three were built; two were exported, while the third, no. 13730 completed in March 1931, was sold to F. Parker & Co. of Ancoates, Manchester. For many years this very interesting tractor has travelled to events from its home base at Boston. One of the exported pair has now returned from South Africa.

Only ten showmen's road locomotives were built by Fodens, and luckily one of them, no. 2104 *Prospector*, built in 1910, has survived into preservation. This engine was supplied new to Walter Shaw of Sheffield and spent its entire working life with them, travelling throughout Yorkshire and the north of England, much of the time operating a Whale switchback.

Road locomotives generally provided another market for Fodens both at home and overseas. Sadly, only a few have survived into preservation. One survivor, 'Colonial' no. 3534 *Monarch*, was the only one of a batch of five to stay in the United Kingdom, spending its working life here. The other four were exported. Early Fodens catalogues offered both compound and single-cylinder road locomotives.

It was not long before Fodens introduced springs on all its engines, including general agricultural designs, both single-cylinder and compound. The tractions were well known for their economy and durability having performed well in trials at Stockport and Newcastle. The Patent spring arrangement reduced shock and vibration, especially when travelling over rough roads, and was much appreciated by the enginemen. It also helped reduce wear and tear. Only seven traction engines survive, one of these having returned home from New Zealand. The oldest survivor is a 6 nhp compound, no. 443 *Victoria*, which was built in 1899; the youngest was built twenty-one years later.

The numbers of surviving wagons and tractors are much higher. The notorious Road Traffic Act of 1930 resulted in many solid-tyred wagons being laid aside, since the operators either had to fit them with pneumatic tyres or pay an excessive road tax, which naturally many companies were reluctant to do. Most companies adopted alternative road transport.

Fodens constructed just ten showmen's road locomotives. Fortunately this one has survived: no. 2104 *Prospector* was completed in March 1910 and was supplied new to W. Shaw & Sons of Sheffield. The engine was to remain with them for its entire working life, travelling the Yorkshire fairgrounds until 1939. *Prospector* is an 8 nhp compound and was purchased for preservation many years ago; it has had several owners since then and is currently to be found in its home county.

This magnificent Foden 8 nhp 'Colonial' road locomotive, no. 3534 built in 1913, was one of five of this type constructed for the overseas market. Four were sent overseas but this one remained in Britain, spending its working life on various duties. At one stage it was with Camel Laird shipbuilders, where it was used for haulage and winching work, and later a different owner used it for agricultural duties. Note the spoked-type flywheel and comparatively small belly tank. This Foden is usually to be seen at the Haddenham rally held in September.

Foden road locomotive no. 4752 *Sandy McNab*, a 6 nhp compound, was completed in 1914 and sold new to an owner in Kilmarnock who used it on agricultural work. In the early 1920s it was sold to Codona Brothers, showmen, who used it for haulage and it ended its working life on agricultural work, this time in Kent, until 1958. In the late 1980s it was converted back to a road locomotive, and was still to be seen, complete with dynamo, at the 1988 Great Dorset Steam Fair.

There are seven surviving Foden traction engines in the British Isles, the oldest of which was constructed in 1899. This 7 nhp compound, no. 2654 *King George V*, was completed in June 1911. It has been in the same family since 1925, having been purchased for use in their threshing business. This picture was taken at the 1995 Astle Park rally.

This Foden 5 ton wagon, no. 1742 *Queen Mary*, was completed in December 1908 and is one of the oldest wagons to survive into preservation. It was sold new to Starkey, Knight & Ford, brewers of Tiverton, Devon, fitted with a box body and towing a trailer. As with many other wagons it was commandeered by the War Department during the First World War for timber haulage. Shortly after the cessation of hostilities it returned to the brewery where it remained until 1931. It was then traded back to Fodens before going on to new owners at Lydney in Glos., where it stayed for thirty years, sadly ending up derelict.

While many engines and wagons have returned home for preservation, others have left our shores. This 4 ton wagon, no. 1364, is one of these, having been sold to an owner at Gotene in Sweden in 1993. The wagon was completed on 24 June 1907 and supplied new to J. Walker, general carriers of Barnsley, Yorkshire, where it worked for nine years. It subsequently changed hands several times. This picture was taken at Lincoln shortly before it went to Sweden.

Most of the companies building steam wagons found themselves very busy on construction for the War Department during the First World War. This Foden 5 ton tipping wagon was completed in December 1917 and sent to France where it was used for transporting materials to repair damaged roads after heavy shelling. After the war it remained in France at a chicory factory at Cambrai, where it was used until 1948. The wagon has now been restored to WD livery. Note the buffers on either side of the smokebox for shunting purposes.

This Foden 'Colonial' wagon was built in 1913 and shipped to Australia where it spent its working life, eventually becoming derelict at Lake Cargelligo nearly a thousand miles from Sydney. It was purchased and shipped home in 1979, and such was the pace of restoration it attended its first rally in 1980 with the paint barely dry. It was not to remain in Britain for long, however, being sold in 1984 to an owner in Stade, Germany. It was shipped out from Hull docks to its new home.

Over the years there have been several important engine sales which naturally attract large crowds of prospective purchasers and other enthusiasts. One important sale was held at W.J. Kings at Bishop Lydeard near Taunton in 1988 when nine very derelict Foden wagons were the principal items. Looking at this picture of the 6 ton tipping wagon, no. 12388, built in 1926, it is difficult to believe that this Foden was among them. Such a high standard of restoration is the result of many hours of painstaking work.

This magnificent example of the Foden 6 ton wagon, works no. 13120, was completed in August 1928 and supplied new to the Openshaw Brewery Co. of Manchester. Just six years later it passed into the ownership of Joseph Ashworth & Son, cattle feed merchants of Frodsham Bridge, Cheshire. It was returned to Fodens to have new wheels and pneumatic tyres fitted. The wagon's final commercial owners were Scientific Roads Ltd, Queensferry, and it remained with them until 1957.

Foden no. 13624 is one of only two HH-type wagons to survive. Built as a three-way tipping wagon, it was completed in December 1929 and was sold to West Riding County Council. It was to have only a short working life as by 1939 it was in Ellis's Scrapyard at Harrogate where it stayed for thirty-one years before being rescued for preservation. The wagon has chain steering instead of the usual Ackerman type, and for a time in preservation it was recorded as no. 13042. For seventeen years it was on display at Penrith Steam Museum.

Members of the Foden works band were transported to and from engagements in a steam bus between 1916 and 1923; unfortunately this did not survive into preservation. Works no. 11340, completed in December 1923, was initially used as a brewer's dray, then it spent some time in the ownership of a Southampton-based showman. It was converted in the late 1950s into a replica of the works bus using the original drawings. For many years it was based in the Norwich area, attending a few local events, after which it moved to the Bygone Village at Fleggburgh. Since then it has again changed owners and now appears in a red livery.

This Foden tractor, works no. 13536, was completed in January 1930. Preserved in the north of England it is often seen at the Pickering rallies which is where this picture was taken.

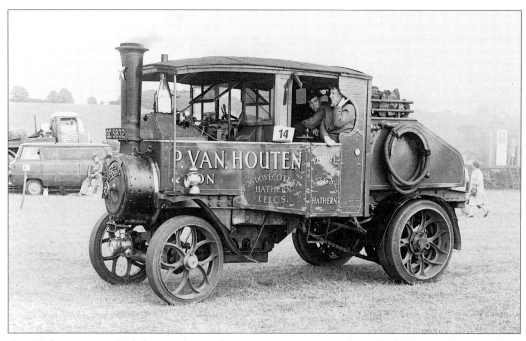

One Foden tractor which has made a welcome reappearance on the rally field is works no. 13196, seen here at Stamford in 1965 on solid rubber tyres. This tractor was supplied new to the Atlas Transport & Shipping Co. Ltd of Chiswick, later moving to Q.M. Camroux & Co. Ltd of Fulham, hence its name *Pride of Fulham*.

Only three Foden 'Sun' or M-type tractors were built. They have distinctive round stainless-steel fireboxes. Works no. 13730 was the only one of the trio to remain in this country, being sold to F. Parker & Co. of Ancoats, Manchester. It has been in preservation at Boston for many years. The other two were exported but one of them has now returned to this country.

This Foden steam wagon, works no. 13008, was completed in June 1928. Its first owner was Belhell & Son of Sale, Cheshire. As with so many steam wagons it was to end its commercial life as a tar sprayer, in the ownership of Penmaenmawr & Trinidad Lake Asphalt Co. Ltd of Bootle. It was rebuilt and shortened to its present form during the 1960s. Another Foden six-wheeler, one of the derelicts in the King's sale, is currently undergoing complete restoration.

Foden D-type tractor, no. 12782 *Angelina*, started life as a timber tractor complete with winch on the rear axle as well as a heavy flywheel and governors for threshing and woodsawing. It was completed in October 1927 and exhibited at the Royal Show held in Newport, and was supplied new to A.W. Brunsdon of Stonehaven, Glos. At that time it was on solid rubber tyres, the pneumatics on the front being a later addition. The Foden has had several owners in preservation.

William Foster & Co. Ltd
Wellington Foundry, Lincoln

There were a number of steam engine builders to be found in and around Lincoln, one of which was Wm Foster & Co. Ltd, and old-established company with a well-deserved high reputation for its products. Like so many of its competitors, the company's first product was a portable engine design. Well before the turn of the century the company had designed and built its first self-moving engine. It was not long before the company became involved in the growing tractor market and in 1904 the first Foster tractor appeared, the forerunner of the famous 'Wellington' tractor. This was to prove a lucrative market for Foster's and the company eventually produced more tractors than traction engine designs. Just over twenty tractors have survived into preservation in the British Isles.

Foster's also produced showmen's road locomotives with considerable success, and eventually became one of the top companies along with market leaders Burrell's and Fowler's. Foster's road locomotives had a high reputation among showmen and several engines have survived. The most familiar of these is no. 14153 *Admiral Beatty*, now part of the Frank Lythgoe collection. Other survivors are two completed in 1920, no. 14501 *Victorious* and no. 14502 *Victory*; the 10 nhp engines no. 14446 *The Leader* and no. 144632 *Success*, the latter based near Hull; and no. 3642 *Maude*, the oldest, built in 1908, and no. 13200 *Aquitania*, a 6 nhp built in 1914.

The company also entered the wagon market both at home and overseas although only 60 wagons were built. An 'overtype' thought to be no. 14470 completed in March 1921 was discovered in Australia in the early 1980s and returned home derelict. This wagon has been fully restored and is the only survivor of its type in the British Isles.

The oldest surviving Foster traction engine is an 8 nhp single no. 2127 built in 1898 and currently to be found in Norfolk, as is no. 2821 constructed in 1903. Another early engine, no. 2163 of 1896 vintage, was at one time part of the famous Holywell collection. Fitted with Starke's Patent valve gear, this 8 nhp single spent most of its working life in Lincolnshire, in the process acquiring a 'Lincolnshire'-type overall canopy. At the other end of the scale is no. 14638, a 5 nhp single built in 1933: this is the company's youngest traction survivor in the British Isles.

Foster's was also involved in the design of a tank for use in the First World War. The first tank was used on the Somme battlefields in 1916. The company's involvement with this type of army equipment was commemorated by the inclusion of a tank in the nameplate ring on the smokebox door. The company ended steam production as it began, producing portable engines until the early 1940s.

Foster's of Lincoln had a high reputation for their showmen's road locomotives, seven of which have fortunately survived the scrapman's cutting torch (although not all are active). Foster 10 nhp no. 14632 *Success* is a fine three-speed compound completed in February 1934. Sold new to Hibble & Mellor, it travelled in the Midlands until 1942 when it was sold for scrap to Hardwicks of Ewell. Still intact, it was purchased in the mid-1950s by Darby's Sand & Gravel Co. of Sutton, Cambs., where it remained for five years before passing into preservation.

During the 1960s many of the showmen's road locomotives were still in the process of restoration and looked very different from their splendid appearance today. This is Foster no. 14153 *Admiral Beatty*, pictured at Chatteris rally in 1963, shortly after the engine had been purchased for preservation. The engine has neither dynamo nor mounting bracket – these had been removed by a previous owner who used the engine for threshing work.

This is *Admiral Beatty* today. Now part of the Frank Lythgoe engine collection, it started life as a road locomotive being purchased by Henry Thurston in 1921 and converted to full showmen's specification. It travelled the fairgrounds for many years before being sold in 1945 by Stanley Thurston to George Desborough & Sons Ltd of Chatteris for agricultural work. It was purchased from Desborough's in 1963 for preservation.

Many of today's showmen's tractors are conversions which have taken place during preservation, but this is not so in the case of Foster 'Wellington' tractor no. 14066 *Endeavour*, built in 1915. During its working life it had several showland owners, including John Beach of Sunbury on Thames and Bert Ayres of Uxbridge. This splendid example of the 'Wellington' tractor underwent a complete overhaul a few years ago. Preserved in Lincolnshire, *Endeavour* is very active during the season and attends many events over a wide area.

This smart Foster 5 ton 4 nhp tractor, no. 13149 *Venture,* was completed in January 1914 and supplied new to J.H. Rundle of New Bolingbroke, being used on general haulage work until commandeered by the government during the First World War. After the war it returned to commercial life. In 1923 it was converted to a showman's tractor and travelled with the same owner on the fairgrounds. As with so many engines, it ended its working days on agricultural work. It was restored in due course and is still with the Rundle family in Lincolnshire.

The 4 nhp 'Wellington' tractor was designed by Foster's to compete with the 4 nhp tractors built by other leading builders. Works no. 14514 *His Grace* was completed in December 1925 and is a particularly fine example. Most of its working life was spent in North Wales. Notice the tank emblem on the smokebox door ring commemorating the company's involvement with tanks during the First World War. The belly tanks also carry the Foster's crest.

Some of the rarest examples of steam engines and wagons which we have today in the British Isles were originally exported and returned home in a very derelict state for preservation. This was the case with Foster 5 ton wagon no. 14470 *Tritton*, completed on 19 March 1921, one of only sixty built by the company. The wagon spent its entire working life in Australia at three different quarries, the last at Port Macquarie in New South Wales where it was still in use until the mid-1940s, after which it became derelict. After purchase it was shipped home on the *Australian Eagle*, arriving in May 1983. The long job of rebuilding included fitting a new boiler barrel, inner firebox and backhead as well as new bearings, regrinding the crankshaft and straightening the chassis. When the mechanical work was completed a new cab and bodywork were fitted, and it was completed in 1988. The wagon is named *Tritton* in recognition of Sir William Tritton, Foster's works manager. The wagon carries the tank emblem on the smokebox door ring.

A typical example of the Foster 7 nhp single-cylinder slide-valve engine design, this is works no. 14422 completed at Lincoln in August 1922. Traction engines used to be a familiar sight on many British farms, often only receiving essential repairs and maintenance, and seldom, if ever, being cleaned, except by the most conscientious engine drivers. This particular Foster can usually be seen at the North Norfolk Railway depot.

This is the oldest Foster traction engine to survive in the British Isles. Works no. 2127 *Jumbo the 4th* was completed in September 1898. It is an 8 nhp single-cylinder slide-valve engine, and one of only two survivors with Starke's Patent valve gear. It was supplied new to Joseph Cade of Whaplode, Lincolnshire, and was eventually abandoned for years, becoming very derelict before being rescued. For a time this engine was at Bressingham Steam Museum.

C.J. Fowell & Co. Ltd
Cromwell Works, St Ives

The town of St Ives in Huntingdonshire is surrounded by agricultural land and hence an ideal location for C.J. Fowell to set up a business constructing traction engines; the company's other principal concern was the repair of agricultural machinery, especially the many steam engines to be found in the area. In all Fowell's built 101 self-propelled engines over the period 1877–1922, five of which were Box Patent road locomotives. The first traction engine, a 6 nhp 4-shaft single, no. 1, was completed in 1878 and sold to Edward Green of North Walsham, Norfolk. Perhaps surprisingly, seven Fowell engines have survived into preservation; all are singles, five of them 7 nhp and two 8 nhp, and one of the former is to be found in Ireland. This number could easily have been higher as several other Fowells were still intact well into the 1950s but subsequently fell victim to the scrapman's torch.

In the early 1960s the late Mr Paisley of Holywell near St Ives took an interest in the engines built by this company, eventually owning three, nos 92 and 97, both 7 nhp, and no. 103, a three-speed 8 nhp, the latter being purchased from Darby's Sand Gravel Co. of Sutton, Cambs. These engines were fully restored and named *Roundhead*, *Ironside* and *Cromwell* respectively. The year 1976 was the centenary of the company and an Expo was held on the East of England Showfield at Alwalton, Peterborough, to mark this event, at which all three engines were present. After Mr Paisley's death the three engines were included in the massive sale held on 1 October 1980. One of the Fowell engines went to an owner in Bedfordshire where it joined no. 91, the oldest survivor, built in 1902. The other two went to more distant parts of the country. Engines nos 91 and 92 occasionally appear together at events in the Eastern Counties.

Many of the engines constructed by Fowell's were sold to local farmers. These engines were equipped with wide wheels which helped to prevent them sinking into the soft ground, especially in local fenland areas, and they were of comparatively light weight compared to some. The front wheels are set further back, making these engines easily recognizable.

The historic market town of St Ives, once a railway junction, has long since lost its railway connections; it has also lost Fowell's which was one time one of the town's principal companies.

Only seven engines built by C.J. Fowell & Co. Ltd have survived. All are single-cylinder slide-valve engines with five being 7 nhp and the other two, including no. 108, being 8 nhp. This engine is the youngest, having been completed in July 1922. Fowell's was one of the smaller builders and it is remarkable that so many of its engines have survived.

This historic picture was taken in October 1993 and shows three of the surviving Fowells outside the (rebuilt) gateway of the former works in New Road, St Ives. What is even more remarkable is that the engines are consecutive numbers: the oldest, no. 91, built in August 1902, is nearest the camera; in the centre is no. 92, built in July 1903; and lastly no. 93, built in December 1904. These dates illustrate the low output from the works: this is explained by the fact that the company also carried out steam engine maintenance, including fitting new boilers and fireboxes, and repaired agricultural machinery.

John Fowler & Co. (Leeds) Ltd
Steam Plough Works, Leeds

The name Fowler is one of the best known in the engine world, the company's wide range of excellent products ensuring that it became well known both at home and overseas. So many of the engines built by this company have survived that enthusiasts would be hard pressed to find an event that does not have at least one Fowler in the line-up, whether it is a traction, roller, ploughing engine or maybe one of the company's 'Tiger' tractors or a massive road engine.

The oldest surviving examples are ploughing engines. The Steam Plough Works began production in 1861 and over the years Fowler's built many ploughing engines and other agricultural implements. In the company's heyday the works provided employment for over 2,500 men on the 15-acre site. The earliest Fowler ploughing engine dates back to 1870: no. 1368 *Margaret* is a 12 nhp single-cylinder design, owned for many years by Beeby Bros of Rempstone. A number of other ploughing engines built in the 1870s also survive: nos 1641 and 1642 are 14 nhp singles dating from 1871, no. 1908 dates from 1873, and there is another of the same type, sadly incomplete. There are also two 14 nhp singles, no. 2013 *Noreen* and no. 2269, of 1873 and 1874 respectively. The two 8 nhp singles restored from a very derelict condition a few years ago are nos 2861 and 3195 of 1876 and 1877.

There are in addition a number of single survivors of other designs: B4 no. 11637 was built in 1909 and K5 no. 12366 *Old Guard*, which worked for many years in East Anglia, was completed in 1910. The 8 nhp single-cylinder piston-valve engine no. 13910, class DDS *My Delight*, was finished in September 1914, and B5 no. 14222 was also built that year. No. 14253 of 1916 was the first of a batch of K7s, classified as a T1 double-drum ploughing engine; this example was for many years in the ownership of Bomford & Evershed and worked until the early 1960s.

By far the most numerous of the survivors are the BB and BB1 class 16 nhp compounds. These were among the company's most successful designs and were very popular with farmers and contractors at home and overseas. Examples were still to be found in use in the 1960s, mostly on dredging and similar work. Many more were to be found at this time lying abandoned where their fire had gone out for the last time. Time and weather took their toll over the years but many of these examples have been rescued for preservation.

Among the other survivors are several K7 class 12 nhp engines. These were built over a long period and the oldest survivor dates back to 1913; the youngest survivors, nos 17756 and 17757, built in 1929, are now owned by Nottingham City Museum. Three class AA6 16 nhp engines dating from 1917 also remain, together with examples of the AA7, AA and AA/ZA classes, all 18 nhp designs. The massive Z7 22 nhp engines were exported to Africa where they were employed on the Sena sugar estates for deep ploughing and other heavy work. Some were in use until the early 1960s. A number have returned to Britain for preservation: many have already been restored while others are still being worked on.

For many years, Fowler's led the market in the production of ploughing engines and equipment, the final examples being completed in 1935. Such is the fascination of these powerful heavy engines that the Steam Plough Club was formed years ago, members often providing working demonstrations of ploughing with reversible ploughs, cultivators and mole drainers.

Fowler's soon progressed into the traction engine market, although no very early examples have survived. The earliest survivor is B1 class no. 6188 *Beulah*, completed at Leeds in August 1890 and supplied new to J.E. Powell of Wrexham, later moving to Cheshire. The engine was later sold by J. Graven & Son of Ely and spent its last working years supplying steam for soil sterilization at a nursery. It was rescued for preservation in 1964 and is now on display at the Bressingham Steam Museum. There are a number of traction engines of various designs from the 1890s in preservation, notably singles and compounds of classes A4, B1, B3, B4 and D2. At the other end of the scale is the A9 class 6 nhp compound no. 21647 *Kinsale*. Built in 1936, this engine was exhibited at Cork Agricultural Show and then sold to a farmer at Minone Bridge, Co. Cork, where it remained until the early 1960s.

Several leading heavy haulage contractors favoured the large Fowler road locomotives for moving heavy, massive and often awkward loads to various destinations in the country. It was not unusual to see as many as three engines hauling one load. The road surfaces and conditions in general presented many problems, such as the need to remove or avoid obstacles en route, obtain water supplies and find overnight parking. Several of the well-known heavy haulage engines are in preservation. One of the best known is B6 class no. 17105 *Atlas*, built in 1928 and supplied new to Norman E. Box of Manchester. Its heavy haulage duties took this engine to many parts of the country. Also completed in 1928 was B6 no. 17106 *Duke of York*. This engine is fitted with a crane and spent most of its working life with Marstons Road Services of Liverpool. Among its many recorded exploits, this engine hauled the rudder of HMS *Ark Royal* from Darlington to Birkenhead in 1939. Completed the following year, B6 crane engine no. 17212 *Wolverhampton Wolverhampton Wanderer* was supplied new to John Thompson of Ettingshall, Wolverhampton, who used this fine example to haul and install 'Lancashire'-type boilers. The Fowler continued on this type of work until the late 1940s when it became the works engine, moving materials around the stock yard.

There are a number of other types of road locomotive in preservation. The army used Fowlers in both the Boer War and the First World War. No. 8894, built in 1901, was used in South Africa hauling guns and supplies; this example returned to the UK in 1996 but there is some uncertainty regarding the works number of this engine. Another ex-War Department engine which made its rally debut in 1996 was B6 class no. 14115 *Lafayette*; this Fowler worked in France during the First World War and on its return passed into the ownership of the London & Kentish Haulage Co. and subsequently other owners until it was laid up in 1946, eventually becoming derelict. It was exhibited in this state on a trailer at Pickering a few years ago but in 1996 it was presented in immaculate condition in WD livery; it has since been repainted blue and now carries the name *The Lion*.

The A4 class 6 nhp road locomotive no. 8712 *Pride of Wales*, completed in July 1900, is one of the oldest surviving Fowler road engines. It was supplied new to J.H. & R.O. Morse, haulage contractors of Norbeth, Pembrokeshire, and spent its life on haulage and driving a stone crusher before being laid up in 1940. It was to be forty years before it was rescued, during which time the weather had inevitably taken its toll.

One very unusual class B6 10 nhp Fowler is no. 17107 built in 1928. This is a powerful stump-puller fitted with a heavy duty winch for pulling out tree stumps and ditch ploughing. It is the only example of its type in the UK, having been preserved near Boston, Lincolnshire, for many years.

A number of magnificent Fowler showmen's road locomotives have survived the years. Notably there are three 'Super Lions'. No. 19783 *King Carnival II*, built in 1932, was supplied new to Mr McConville, showman of West Hartlepool, Co. Durham. No. 19782 *The Lion*, also of 1932, was supplied to Anderton & Rowland; laid up for many years, *The Lion* has since changed hands and is currently undergoing full restoration. No. 20223 *Supreme*, the last showman's built by Fowler's in 1934, went to Mrs A. Deakin & Sons of Brynmawr, South Wales. This engine was built to special order with chrome fittings and left-hand steering. It was commandeered for heavy haulage in the Glasgow area during the Second World War. *Supreme* is now to be seen at the National Motor Museum, Beaulieu. Only four of these 'Super Lion' showman's engines were constructed, the fourth, no. 19989 *Onward*, built in 1933 and supplied to S. Ingham, has unfortunately not survived.

Among the other splendid surviving Fowler showmen's engines are R3 class nos 15652 and 15653 *Repulse* and *Renown*, both built in 1920 and supplied to John Murphy of Gateshead; B class no. 14424 *Valiant* and no. 14425 *Carry On*; and the one known to many for its role in the famous film *The Iron Maiden*, R3 class no. 15657 *Kitchener*, was originally used for stone haulage by Portland Stone Quarries but was later converted to full showman's specification for Mrs H. Oadley of Derbyshire.

Fowler's came very late to the wagon market and it was not until 1924 that the company's first designs appeared, being introduced at the Royal Show held at Leicester that year. By this time, however, sales of steam wagons were already on the decline, petrol-driven vehicles already becoming established. In all Fowler's only constructed 124 wagons, most of which went to the UK market, only a small number going abroad. Production lasted for just seven years. In 1931 Fowler's produced its final design; more powerful than its predecessors, just five were built before the decision to cease wagon production was taken.

Fowler's also constructed thirty-eight gully emptiers. One of these was no. 19708, completed in December 1931 and supplied to City of Leeds where it worked until 1941.

It is a remarkable survival. After being laid aside it ended up at Robinson & Burdsells, Hunslet, where it gradually disappeared under a heap of scrap metal; then, in 1961, it was cut up. Seven years later, still in pieces, it was rescued for preservation although with many parts missing. Then began the long, involved and expensive task of rebuilding the wagon; it is the only survivor of the gully emptiers built by the company.

Other surviving Fowlers include a number of tractors of the 'Hercules' and 'Tiger' designs as well as a great many road-rollers. These were a familiar sight over the years building and repairing the highways, and some were still to be found at work in the 1960s. The earliest survivor is D class no. 7129 *Alice* of 1894, one of only three survivors built before the turn of the century. For many years rollers were a very important part of the company's output and the youngest survivor is DNB class no. 22596 *Evening Star*, completed in December 1937. The surviving rollers are of several designs. One very interesting example is N class no. 12530 built in 1912 which is thought to be the only survivor of its type, most of this design having been sold overseas. No. 12530 was supplied to Durham County Council where it proved to be ideal for the often hilly terrain which it encountered during its work.

Fowler's of Leeds deserves a book of its own, and it is only possible to mention just a few of the engines here. As would be expected from a large company with a lively overseas market, many examples from abroad have survived, as well as those in the British Isles.

Fowler showman's road locomotive no. 15657 *The Iron Maiden* moves slowly around the field at Stamford rally, 1965. Supplied new to Portland Stone Quarries it was used initially on road haulage work but was later converted to full showman's specification for Mrs H. Oadley of Derbyshire carrying the name *Kitchener*. This engine became widely known through its appearance on cinema and television screens as *The Iron Maiden*.

Fowler's of Leeds was well known for its road locomotives, both for showman's use and heavy haulage generally. No. 11108 *Dreadnought*, one of several showman's to carry this name, was built in 1909 and is a 7 nhp compound class A5 design. During its working life it travelled with Coles' Venetian gondolas. For many years this engine was preserved in East Anglia before moving to new owners in the north.

Some showmen's road locomotives were built to special order and Fowler no. 15653 *Renown* is one of them. Together with its sister engine *Repulse*, it was owned by John Murphy of Gateshead, Co. Durham, travelling with his Proud scenic peacock ride, becoming well-known in the north of England. *Renown* was completed in May 1920 and is an example of the company's 8 nhp R3 design. During the war both engines were used on timber work.

Another engine built to special order was the Fowler showman's road locomotive *Supreme*. The last showman's to be built by Fowler's, it was completed in March 1934 for Mrs A. Deakin & Son of Brynmawr and it travelled the fairgrounds until the Second World War when it was commandeered to haul railway locomotives from a Glasgow works to the docks. *Supreme* ended up at Hardwicks scrapyard from where it was rescued, and it is now in trust at the National Motor Museum, Beaulieu.

The massive Fowler crane engines always attract attention. Works no. 17106 *Duke of York*, a B6 design, was built in 1928 and spent most of its working life hauling huge, extremely heavy loads for Marstons Road Services Ltd. While with this company the Fowler was not named but was usually referred to as 'The Big Engine'. It is seen here with the crane jib removed.

Over the years this fine 10 nhp Fowler crane locomotive *Wolverhampton Wanderer*, works no. 17212, has been seen at a great many events both at home and in Europe. This B6 'Super Lion' was completed in June 1929 and supplied new to John Thompson of Ettingshall, Wolverhampton. It was used to deliver 'Lancashire'-type boilers all over the country; these were large difficult loads requiring considerable planning. It was used on this work until 1948 when it became the company's yard engine.

The oldest surviving Fowler crane engine is no. 8920 *The Great North*, built in 1901. This 8 nhp B5 class was supplied new to Stuart Dodds of Leith and just three years later John Wilkinson purchased the assets of this heavy engineering company. The Fowler worked until 1927, after which it spend thirty years in a shed. It was repainted to celebrate the company's 110 years in business after which it was eventually sold for preservation.

This Fowler 10 nhp B5 road engine returned from South Africa in 1996. It is believed to be no. 8894, one of four armour-clads, as they were known, sent out in 1900 for use by the Royal Engineers during the Boer War. The heavy armour was then removed and the Fowler used to haul guns and supplies. In due course it was sold, being used for agricultural duties until the mid-1930s. It is currently undergoing restoration, which should enable its identification to be confirmed.

This A9 class Fowler road locomotive will be remembered by many readers for the journey it made in 1966, hauling the new railway locomotive *River Mite* from York to Ravenglass in Cumbria, over a difficult and hilly route across the Pennines. The engine is works no. 15649 *Providence*, built in 1920. It is an excellent example of the company's 7 nhp A9 design.

This 7 nhp A8 class Fowler, no. 13922 *Girly*, was built as a road locomotive in 1913, spending its first years on haulage work. Six years later it was converted to showman's specification by Charles Openshaw of Reading. During its life on the northern fairgrounds it was owned by John Hoadley and later Slaters Amusements of Carlisle before being laid up at the outbreak of the Second World War.

One of the best known of all the Fowler road locomotives has to be B6 class *Ajax*. Built in 1928, it was supplied to Norman E. Box, haulage contractors of Manchester. No. 17105, *Ajax* is the sole survivor of the fleet of Fowlers once operated by this well-known company. These engines hauled massive loads throughout the British Isles, moving heavy castings, transformers, boilers and even more difficult tasks with ease.

Engines that spent their working lives overseas are still being brought back. This 6 nhp Fowler road locomotive, no. 12275 built in 1910, spent its working life in New Zealand before returning home in 1995. It made its first public appearance at the 1996 Fowler display at the Great Dorset Steam Fair, where this picture was taken.

Some readers may recall this 8 nhp Fowler B6 road engine, no. 14115, on display at Pickering rally a few years ago in a very derelict condition. Fully restored, it made its rally debut in 1996 in WD livery carrying the name *Lafayette*. Since then it has received blue livery and the name *The Lion*. This fine engine was built in 1914 and supplied to the War Department at the start of the First World War. In 1918 it was sold to London Traction Haulage, which was taken over by Pickfords in 1921, and then to Walter Denton of Hyde, Manchester, in 1932. It was laid up in 1947, eventually becoming derelict, until rescued for preservation.

In 1920 Robert Wynn & Sons, haulage contractors of Newport, took delivery of this powerful 7 nhp class A9 Fowler road locomotive, no. 15463 *Dreadnought*. After the 1930s the engine stood on Cardiff Docks until the early 1960s when it was taken to the company's Newport depot and rebuilt to celebrate the company's centenary in 1963. It then went into storage. It is preserved in South Wales.

During the 1970s this 5 nhp Fowler D2 road locomotive was preserved at Taunton in Somerset. Works no. 12899 *Western Star* was built in 1912 and supplied new to Carmarthen County Council who used it for stone hauling. In 1922 it was purchased by a contractor to drive a sawmill and was also used on threshing work. *Western Star* has now been in preservation in Yorkshire for a number of years.

This Fowler traction engine is an excellent example of the company's A4 class design. It was built in 1902 as works no. 9230, a 6 nhp single-cylinder engine. The oldest surviving A4 in the British Isles was built at the Leeds works in 1895.

One of the most popular engine names is *Dreadnought*: there are quite a number in preservation and doubtless many others which also carried this name have been scrapped. This is a splendid example of the Fowler A8 design, works no. 11491, built in 1909 and supplied new to Mr Daws of Mileham, Norfolk, where it spent its working life.

Two contrasting Fowler designs: 'Colonial' BAA class no. 10773 is a 6 nhp single-cylinder design completed in July 1907 and exported to Australia. This type was designed to burn wood or straw, not coal, and is easily recognizable by the unusual chimney. The one nearest the camera is of a more traditional design.

This Fowler traction engine has been a familiar sight at East Anglian rallies for many years. A 7 nhp R class compound, no. 10373 *Ada* was completed in October 1905 and supplied to Lord Ellesmere of Stetchworth Hall, Newmarket, where it was used on threshing and general agricultural duties. It was purchased for preservation in 1947.

This massive Fowler B6 'Super Lion' stump puller is the only example of its kind in the British Isles. Built in 1928 as works no. 17107, it is a 10 nhp compound fitted with a very heavy duty winch and rope for ditch ploughing and tree stump pulling. The massive rear wheels are 7 feet in diameter and 26 inches wide, and the engine weighs in at 20 tons.

Fowler's received an order for 150 8 nhp type TE2 haulage and winding engines for Russia but because of the revolution there not all of them were sent, the remainder being sold on to the home market. This one, works no. 14933 *Challenger*, was completed in November 1917 and sold to R. Hardy, a threshing contractor at Helpringham, where it spent its working life. It has been in preservation for forty years at Boston, Lincolnshire.

Low autumn sunshine highlights some of the features on this Fowler 14 nhp single-cylinder ploughing engine. Works no. 1642, built in 1871, is ready for a demonstration run at the British National Ploughing Championships near Newark in 1992. The oval plate on the boiler is not the works plate – it reads Beeby Brothers no. 4 set.

This 8 nhp DDS class Fowler ploughing engine, works no. 13910 *My Delight*, is thought to be the only survivor of its type. It is a single-cylinder piston-valve engine completed in September 1914. Fowler's introduced many designs over the years, some of which are now represented by single examples.

Still undergoing restoration when this picture was taken, this is Fowler B4 class works no. 11637, a 14 nhp double-crank compound design built in 1909. This engine was supplied new to T.O. Newman of Stansted. Prior to its return to steam in 1991 it had been abandoned for over forty years. In the background is the sole surviving Howard ploughing engine.

Two of these massive Z7 Fowlers were in the auction held at the 1988 Great Dorset Steam Fair. Nos 15509/10 were built in 1920 and spent their working lives in Africa. Luckily, the dry climate prevented too much deterioration during the period which they were laid aside. Both engines have since been fully restored and are preserved near Bedford.

One of the oldest surviving Fowler ploughing engines, this is works no. 1368 *Margaret*, built in 1870. A 12 nhp single-cylinder design, it was owned for many years by Beeby Brothers of Rempstone who at one time operated several ploughing sets. The heavy soil at the Great Dorset Steam Fair stuck to the 'spuds' fitted on the rear wheels.

The BB1 class of Fowler ploughing engines has the largest number of surviving examples. Powerful 16 nhp double-crank compound engines, they were highly thought of by farmers and contractors. No. 15163 was completed in May 1918 and sold to the War Department, later passing into the ownership of G. Gunter of Wetherby, Yorkshire. It is now preserved in Cornwall.

Gleaming like a new pin despite the rather grey weather conditions at Pickering, this is 16 nhp BB class no. 14375, built in 1917 and supplied new to Wards of Carrington, Lincolnshire. It is in preservation in the same county. This picture clearly shows the wire rope and drum on this engine.

Another fine example of the Fowler BB1 class is preserved in Ireland. Works no. 15223 *Paddy* was completed in September 1918 and spent part of its working life in Lincolnshire. It later passed to Bomford & Carr of Stratford-upon-Avon. This picture was taken at the Fowler event held at the 1996 Great Dorset Steam Fair.

The wide open spaces, huge camping area and car parks can only be the Great Dorset Steam Fair. Here Fowler Z7 class no. 15670 backs slowly down the hill for demonstration purposes. This engine was one of several supplied new to the Sena sugar estates at Lumbo in Mozambique in 1922 where they were used for deep ploughing and cultivating until the early 1960s. This massive 22 nhp DCC returned to Britain in 1977.

Two veteran Fowlers, both 8 nhp singles: on the left is no. 2861 built in 1876 and nearest the camera no. 3195 of 1877. These are the famous 'Inkbarrow' engines which lay derelict for many years and were generally thought to be beyond restoration when rescued in 1989. However, painstaking work has returned these two splendid engines, which last worked in 1936, to superb condition.

This is another veteran Fowler which was for many years operated by Beeby Brothers of Rempstone. Works no. 2013 *Noreen* was built in 1873 as a 14 nhp single-cylinder design. The Beeby Brothers plate can be seen on the side of the boiler. Eight Fowler ploughing engines built in the 1870s still survive in the British Isles.

Several sets of Fowler ploughing engines have been converted to diesel power using a variety of units originally built by McLaren or Mercedes, and others taken from Sherman tanks. No. 14380, a class BB built in 1917, is one of a pair fitted with boiler-mounted six-cylinder McLaren engines.

No engine builder could afford to neglect the lucrative steamroller market. Fowler's of Leeds certainly became heavily involved with these engines. This superbly restored example, works no. 18867 *Ida*, a 4 nhp, was originally built for export in 1934 but was never sent; instead it was purchased in 1938 by Louth Borough Council and it is still preserved in the same town where it spent most of its working life.

This 12 ton class DNB single-cylinder roller was completed at Leeds in March 1930 as works no. 18659. It was supplied new to Portugal and returned to this country in 1976. It now carries the name *Arfur*.

Many rollers were still to be found in action well into the 1960s. Fowler no. 15902, a D5 class 12 ton model built in 1923, did not quite make it to the 1960s, retiring in 1959 after spending its entire working life with Ashford District Council. Since being rescued for preservation it has had several owners. Notice the Fowler crest in front of the flywheel.

This N class roller is thought to be the only surviving example, but as most of this type were exported it is not beyond the realms of possibility that one may survive somewhere. This 7 ton single-cylinder roller, works no. 12530 *Bellingham*, was completed in May 1912 and supplied to Durham County Council where it was found to be particularly suitable for the hilly terrain.

This T3 class tractor, works no. 16365 *King of the Road*, was supplied new to the Dunster Castle estate. It was later acquired by highways contractors Eddisons, and converted into a roller. Conversion back to its present form took place in the mid-1960s while it was preserved in Yorkshire. The engine is a 4 nhp compound completed in July 1928.

Fowler's of Leeds came late to the lucrative wagon market, producing their first designs in 1924. However, petrol lorries had already become well established and the steam wagon market was on the decline. This 6 ton Fowler was completed in December 1931 and supplied to the City of Leeds as a gully emptier. It worked until 1941 when it was sold to Robinson & Birdsell, eventually becoming covered with scrap. In 1961 it was cut up, but was rescued a few years later, albeit with many parts missing, and restored as the only surviving Fowler wagon in the British Isles. When this picture was taken in the 1980s it was in blue livery but it has since been repainted green.

Richard Garrett & Sons Ltd
Leiston, Suffolk

When this well-known East Anglian company introduced its 4CD tractor in 1907 it was hardly expected to become the company's most successful design, with 514 being constructed over a twenty-one year period. During the First World War a considerable number of these very useful tractors were built for government use, and after wartime service many went into private ownership, purchased from the numerous surplus equipment sales which took place after the war.

The 4CD tractor was also exported as both standard and colonial models, and the basic design was also used for a steamroller produced by the company. A large number of 4CDs have survived, together with a handful of rollers. They were extensively advertised immediately after the war for road haulage, timber work, farm duties and threshing, only a few being supplied to showmen to haul lighter loads. The advertising campaign must have proved successful as the company produced a considerable number of tractors during 1919 and the early 1920s. Doubtless sales would have been depressed by the surplus war equipment flooding the market, although the condition of many of the ex-WD engines meant that they would have required extensive work.

The first engine produced by the company was a portable, in the early 1840s. Within a comparatively short time the first self-propelled design was introduced. The first geared traction engine was constructed in 1876, fitted with the company's patent corrugated firebox, a successful innovation that was to become standard on most engines built by the company.

Despite the competition Garrett's encountered from the other builders in eastern England, the works produced a steady stream of traction engines in 6, 7 and 8 nhp designs. In the early 1900s a number of large three-speed compound road locomotives were built, some of which being exported to South Africa, New Zealand and Mauritius. The South African engines had 'colonial' fireboxes.

In December 1909 a 6 nhp two-speed compound road locomotive, no. 27946, was completed and supplied new to J. Harkness of Belfast. It remained with the company, working for fifty-eight years, and on retirement it passed straight into preservation. Although Garrett's built a few showmen's road locomotives, none of these has survived. Other road engines were converted to showman's specification after starting life on haulage work. One such example has recently undergone a complete restoration: built in 1908, no. 27160 was named *Crimson Lady* in the early years of preservation but in the early 1990s it changed hands and has now regained its original name, *British Hero*. It returned to the rally fields in 1997, albeit still under restoration.

In 1918 Garrett's introduced a steam tractor known as the 'Suffolk Punch' or 'Agrimotor' which was designed for direct ploughing. With internal combustion engine tractors becoming widely available this design faced fierce competition from the onset and only a small number were built. Although it was a well thought out design incorporating several new features, it was not popular and only one example, no. 33130 built in 1919, survives. This engine has been seen on the rally fields for many years and in 1993 passed into the ownership of the Long Shop Museum at Leiston.

Garrett's was one of several builders who began to explore the wagon market shortly after the turn of the twentieth century. Production commenced with a 5 ton overtype design in 1908, and during the following years a large number of this type were built in 3, 4, 5 and (in the 1920s) 6 ton models for both the home and overseas markets. In 1922 a four-wheeled 6 ton undertype appeared, and six years later a six-wheeler was added to the range. The wagons were constructed with various types of body for different uses. The QL class was very advanced for its day boasting Ackerman steering; the later examples also had pneumatic tyres and other improvements. At least one of the overtypes survives: no. 34932, a 6 ton model, was built in 1926 and is now in Canada. There are also several undertypes in various parts of Britain although not all are complete. Over the years the wagon market became a very important and lucrative part of the company's business.

The oldest surviving traction engine built by the company in the British Isles is a 6 nhp single, no. 23992, completed in November 1902. Garrett's was involved with construction of traction engines over a long period, but despite this only fourteen have survived in the British Isles. One example, originally supplied to the Norfolk Motor Transport Co. of Norwich in 1918, is no. 33068, a 6 nhp compound. It was originally fitted with a belly tank for haulage work and after several owners it ended its working days in Yorkshire, eventually becoming part of the well-known Philp collection which included many unrestored and derelict engines. The Garrett spent a number of years with some limited protection from the elements; it was the star item at the Philp sale held in June 1995 and it is currently undergoing restoration.

Garrett's continued building traction engines into the 1930s although most of those built during the 1920s and 1930s were destined for overseas markets, home demand for traction engines having reduced dramatically at this time. The last built, no. 35461, a 6 nhp single completed in June 1931, still survives.

The majority of the rollers built at Leiston were based on the popular 4CD design, while others were orthodox single-cylinder designs in various weights. Two very derelict 4CD rollers were included in the Philp sale; both required extensive rebuilding but just two years later one of them has been fully restored – a remarkable effort in view of the roller's condition when sold. Garrett's exported many 4CD rollers, most of which were supplied to the continent. The highest number of surviving Garrett rollers is to be found in Switzerland where there are three in private hands and one in the splendid Lucerne Transport Museum. (There are incidentally a considerable number of other British-built rollers in Switzerland, with examples of Aveling & Porter, Fowler, and Wallis & Steevens designs, the latter all of the company's 'Advance' type.)

Garrett's became associated with the Agricultural & General Engineers Ltd, an amalgamation of several of the leading engine builders which formed in 1920 and lasted until 1932. In July 1928 an announcement was made to the effect that the range of products formerly offered by Burrell's would in future be undertaken by Garrett's, to whom all future enquiries and orders should be forwarded. Several engines were completed after this announcement, including the 8 nhp showman's road locomotive no. 4092 *Simplicity*, ordered by Mrs A. Deakin of Brynmawr which was dispatched to its owner in October 1930, but sadly has not survived. In 1932 the major interest in Garrett's was secured by the well-known railway locomotive building company Beyer, Peacock & Co. Ltd of Gorton Foundry, Manchester, whereupon the company name changed for the last time to the Richard Garrett Engineering Works Ltd.

This Garrett 6 nhp compound road locomotive, no. 27946 *Vera*, passed straight from its working life into preservation. Completed in December 1909, it was sold to J. Harkness of Belfast where it remained in use until 1967, establishing what is almost certainly a record for the longest period of service by a road locomotive in the British Isles.

This is the only surviving Garrett showman's road locomotive, no. 27160 *British Hero*, completed in June 1908. This engine started life on general haulage but it was later converted to a showman's engine for Thomas Sheppard of Wellingborough, when it was renamed *Crimson Lady* and travelled with a set of three-abreast gallopers. In 1935 it was sold to Rundles of New Bolingbroke and used for agricultural work. The engine was last seen at a rally in 1960 after which it stood for many years until acquired by its present joint owners in 1991. Following a very extensive rebuild it appeared in public once again in 1997 and it is pictured here on its way to its first event in wet gloomy conditions.

This Garrett tractor was originally ordered by the War Department as a crane engine, but the order was cancelled and no. 33486 *Queen of Great Britain*, built in 1919, was sold to Browing Bros, haulage contractors of Stonehouse, Glos. In 1921 the engine passed into the ownership of W. & J. Cole, amusement caterers of Bristol, who had it converted to showland use. For over thirty years it travelled in the west country with a set of gallopers and chair o' planes, passing into preservation in the mid-1950s. This is one of the few Garrett tractors with a showland history.

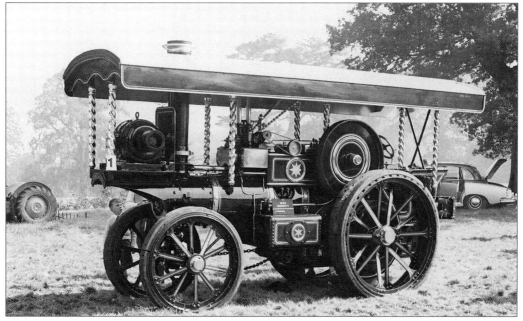

This is Garrett showman's tractor no. 33902 *Medina* pictured at the 1963 Raynham Day. This 4CD tractor was completed in August 1920. For many years it has been in the ownership of Thursford Steam Museum, on display as a static exhibit.

The 4CD tractor was unquestionably one of the most successful Garrett designs, and they were built over a long period of time. They were popular for many types of haulage work, particularly for timber haulage work. No. 34539 *Evelyn* was completed in June 1924. It is a fine example of this well-proven design.

This is 4CD tractor no. 33380 at Chatteris rally in 1963. This engine, one of the large batch built for the government during the First World War, was not completed until October 1918, just prior to the cessation of hostilities. This engine looks very different now, having been converted to showman's specification in preservation; it now appears in blue livery under the name *Sapphire*.

During 1918 the majority of Garrett's production of 4CD tractors was for government use, and in one month ten were constructed, among them no. 33296 *Adventurer*, completed on 22 May 1918. Large sales of surplus equipment were held after the First World War, and *Adventurer* was purchased by E.W. Farrow of Spalding for use on general haulage. In 1941 it was with Carter Bros of Billinghurst, where it was employed on timber work.

This Garrett 4CD is part of the Bressingham Steam Museum collection. No. 34641 was completed in 'Exhibition finish' special chocolate livery with red wheels for the 1924 Smithfield Show. It was sold to Clare Urban District Council in 1925 complete with two wagons to haul stone for road construction and repair. The engine underwent a complete rebuild in the early 1990s.

The 'Suffolk Punch' was a unique and unconventional design produced by Garrett's in an attempt to counter the increasing numbers of internal combustion tractors. While the design was well thought out, having chain drive and controls similar to a motor car's which made it very manoeuvrable, it did not catch on and only one survives, no. 33180, now at the Long Shop Museum, Leiston. This engine was designed to plough six furrows directly. It was shipped new to Mr Goddard of Tunstall, Suffolk, but was not suitable for the heavy wet soil conditions there and spent most of its life driving machinery instead.

This 6 nhp single-cylinder traction engine is a Garrett design of which only five were built. No. 34045 was completed in July 1921. The engine was owned by Mr Hamment of Bergh Apton and later went to rallies until the early 1970s. This picture was taken at Weeting rally – an event it has attended several times.

The Philp collection sale held on Saturday 24 June 1995 attracted people from all over the British Isles and overseas. The star attraction was this 6 nhp Garrett compound traction engine, no. 33068, completed on 6 June 1918, which had been kept at the farm since 1946 under limited shelter. Supplied new to the Norfolk Motor Transport Co. of Norwich, this engine passed three years later to J.E. Kirby & Sons of Martham. In 1925 it moved on to Wm A. Green, timber merchants of North Walsham, and in 1934 moved north to Edwin Knowles of Braithwell in Yorkshire. The Garrett was originally fitted with belly tanks for long-haul road work.

Garrett's of Leiston built a total of 310 undertype wagons, of which only four, all QL class examples, survive in the British Isles. Works no. 35465, completed in July 1931, is the youngest survivor. Garrett wagons were supplied to both the home and overseas markets. This picture was taken in 1976.

One of the best-known Garrett engines in East Anglia, this is no. 32396 *Felsted Belle*, pictured here over twenty-five years ago at a Wisbech rally. Built in 1916, this 7 nhp single-cylinder engine was supplied to Messrs Blewitts of Cornish Hall End but shortly after arrival it was requisitioned by the War Department and sent over to France. After its return, the engine spent its working life in East Anglia. The Garrett has now been on the rally scene for well over forty years.

Garrett wagon no. 35465 as it looks in 1997, resplendent in a shiny black livery. This Garrett spent its working life in the west country, initially with Glover & Uglow Ltd of Callington, Cornwall, and in later years with Cornwall County Council, ending its days in a quarry in Devon from where it was rescued for preservation.

There were two very derelict Garrett 10 ton rollers in the Philp collection sale. No. 34706 *The London Belle* came apart during the struggle to free it from the undergrowth, weather conditions having taken their toll. Completed on 3 March 1925, it was sold new to Zachariah Fairclough of Clacton on Sea, supplied through George Thurlow & Sons, engine dealers of Stowmarket. It had two other commercial owners, both in Suffolk, before being purchased for the collection in 1964. Despite its condition the Garrett was sold and will certainly be a long-term restoration project.

This fine example of the CD Garrett 10 ton roller, no. 34084 *The Baroness*, was completed on 3 February 1922 and supplied to Suffolk County Council, who used it mainly in the Ipswich area until the early 1950s after which it was sold to Bligo & Harrison. Preserved in Cheshire, it has been seen at numerous events, notably here at the Weeting rally.

T. Green & Sons Ltd
Smithfield Iron Works, Leeds

Leeds was an important place for the construction of steam locomotives generally, with several companies located there building both road and railway locomotives. One of these companies was Thomas Green & Sons Ltd, situated in North Street. The only remaining engines built by this company in the British Isles are all single-cylinder slide-valve rollers, the oldest dating back to 1894, the youngest completed in June 1927. Green's had both a home and overseas market, continuing to build both single cylinder and compound rollers until the early 1930s. The company also ventured into other markets, in 1911 advertising single-cylinder and compound tractors convertible to steamrollers.

Rollers in preservation are of several weights. No. 1508 of 1894 and no. 1968 of 1917 are both 8 ton models supplied new to Derby Corporation and the War Department respectively. No. 1978, built in 1921, is a 9 ton model, while nos 2007 and 2054 of 1920 and 1927 are of the 10 ton design. In the early 1990s only one example of Green's rollers was generally to be found on the rally field, no. 1968 *Rose* which worked for Devon County Council.

All five of the remaining rollers built by Green's in the British Isles are single-cylinder designs. No. 1968 *Rose*, an 8 ton roller, was completed in June 1917 and supplied to the War Department for use on road repairs in France. It later passed into the ownership of Devon County Council and remained with them until the 1970s. This splendid roller appears at events mostly in the west country.

J. & F. Howard
Britannia Iron Works, Bedford

A few years ago you would have had to travel a long way to see one of this company's engines but today two very interesting examples are to be found in Britain. The first of these returned home in a derelict condition, with many parts missing. No. 201, an 8 nhp single-cylinder engine built in 1872, was shipped out to Australia, ending up at Dukes Aramac, about a thousand miles from Brisbane. Details of its subsequent history are very sketchy but it is thought to have worked on a sheep-shearing plant in 1908. It was rescued for preservation, shipped home and fully restored, making its rally debut at the 1983 Expo held over the August Bank holiday at the East of England showground at Alwalton, Peterborough. It attracted enormous attention, nothing like it having previously been seen on the rally field. It was later to return to its birthplace where it was posed for photographs outside the impressive gates of the Britannia Iron Works. It is currently at the Beamish Museum.

The second of the two surviving Howards is every bit as fascinating. This ploughing engine, works number unknown, is believed to have been built in 1876. Little is known of its early history, but it was purchased by Baldwin Bros of Wadhurst, Sussex, in 1916 and remained with them until 1929 when it was sold to the Henry Ford Museum in the America, only returning home in 1991. When restored, it will attract much attention as it is very different in operation to the conventional ploughing engines, its flywheel being located between the rear wheels; it also has a pair of rear-mounted cable drums.

The very distinctive lines of a Howard traction engine can be clearly seen from this broadside picture of no. 201 *Britannia*, built in 1872. This 8 nhp single-cylinder traction spent its working life in Australia and returned home derelict. After complete restoration by the late Tom Varley it attracted much attention, being very different to those with which we are familiar. For a time it was the only example of a Howard engine in the British Isles. It is currently to be found at the Beamish Museum.

In 1991 a second Howard arrived back in Britain. This early ploughing engine – built in 1876 – had been in the Henry Ford Museum in the United States for sixty-two years. Its works number is unknown, and nothing is known of its very early history. The engine is complete and will certainly attract considerable attention when it is back in steam.

Leyland Motors Ltd
Leyland, Lancashire

Although Leyland built a considerable number of wagons only two have survived. One of these is in the Commercial Vehicle Museum at Leyland, the other is in private ownership and currently undergoing restoration. Both are F2 models, the first built in 1923 and the other thought to have been constructed in the following year. Leyland steam vehicles were produced up to 1926. The company also built steam-powered vans, wagons and buses. As development of the internal combustion engine gathered pace, so the government placed contracts for petrol lorries to serve in the First World War; this created space problems for Leyland so the company purchased an empty mill at Chorley where steam production could continue, but then the decision was taken to halt steam construction until after the war. In 1919 Leyland Motors Ltd was formed and recommenced production of steam vehicles. But the writing was on the wall for steam wagons by the mid-1920s and with declining sales the range was first reduced and

For many years this was the only example of the Leyland F2 wagon in Britain; built in 1923, it was found derelict in Northern Queensland and brought back in 1968 to be restored at Leyland. At the time of writing a second Leyland, built in around 1924, is nearing completion.

eventually ceased entirely in 1926, any spares being transferred to Atkinson's, who took over responsibility for the Leyland steam vehicles leaving Leyland to concentrate on their range of internal combustion vehicles.

During their years of steam production Leyland built up both home and overseas markets. This explains the discovery of a very derelict wagon in Northern Queensland, Australia, where it was thought to have worked at various logging sites in the area. Eventually this wagon was crated and shipped back to Britain. Complete restoration was commenced by works apprentices in early 1968, and after two years of painstaking work the project finally emerged in all its glory, attracting considerable attention. This wagon has been seen at a few events and is now at the Commercial Vehicle Museum.

Mann Patent Steam Cart & Wagon Co. Ltd
Pepper Road, Leeds

The Mann works was situated at Pepper Road in the Hunslet district of Leeds, an area well known for several steam engine building companies. Only a small number of Mann engines and wagons have survived into preservation. In addition there is one patching roller which has two rolls at the front and one at the rear; built in 1919 this is currently preserved in Somerset. Mann wagons were available with a wide range of bodies for various applications, including box vans and bodies suitable for brewers, millers, market gardeners and general loads.

One survivor which for many years appeared at events over a wide area while preserved in Lincolnshire has since left Britain and is now to be found in Holland. This is the tractor no. 1425 *Little Jim*, built in 1920. Another widely travelled tractor is no. 1325 *Myfanwy*, completed in 1918, which spent its entire working life on Anglesey where it remains in preservation. The engine was owned by a farming co-operative, and among its varied duties were threshing, haulage and wood-sawing. No. 1343 *Lizer*, built five months later, is currently on display as a static exhibit at Bressingham Steam Museum. *Old King Cole*, no. 1260, built in 1917 and supplied to a farmer at Royston, Herts., is now to be found in the Hollycombe collection. It spent its working life on direct ploughing, threshing, wood cutting and haulage work – it really was the steam equivalent of today's all-purpose tractors. For a number of years it was preserved in the Leeds area, becoming well known at many of the Yorkshire rallies to which it travelled under its own steam.

The oldest surviving Mann has a very interesting history. No. 881 was built in 1914 for the War Department and was used for gun haulage in France during the First World War; it returned home in due course and was sold to Fylde Council, which in turn sold it on to Isaac Balls, a road-builder based in Southport, Lancashire. The engine was then converted into a roller and used in the north-west. In preservation it has been rebuilt once again, this time as a wagon.

Three other Mann wagons survive. No. 1120, an overtype 5 tonner built in 1916, was rescued for preservation in 1960 and can be seen at events with a container resplendent in brown livery and lettered T. Frampton Contractors, Farnham, this company having used the Mann during its commercial life for furniture haulage and removal work. There are also several other tractors in preservation.

The company also produced other types which have no survivors, such as the 5/6 ton undertype wagon known as the 'Express'; this design was available with many different bodies including one with compartment boxes which could tip either side independently.

The Mann Patent Steam Cart & Wagon Co. Ltd, a formidable company name, is represented in the British Isles by twelve examples built over a fourteen-year period, the majority of which are tractors. This example, no. 1325 *Myfanwy*, was completed in October 1918. The engine was owned by a farming co-operative and spent all its working life on Anglesey on threshing, haulage and wood-sawing. It is one of only two surviving examples of its type.

In addition wagons were also available specially equipped as municipal vehicles, particularly for gully emptying, street watering and tar spraying.

Prior to the formation of this company, traction engines were produced by Mann & Charlesworth at Canning Works, Dewsbury Road, Leeds, but none of these early examples has survived into preservation. As with so many other companies, the Mann Patent Steam Cart & Wagon Co. Ltd also had an export market, particularly to Australia. Unfortunately the vast majority of Mann's records were destroyed when the company closed.

Mann single-cylinder tractor no. 1420 *Little Jim*, built in 1920, was a familiar sight for many years at events in eastern England and further afield from its base in Lincolnshire. It is now preserved in Holland, having been purchased at the Penrith Museum auction in 1994. This picture was taken in the early 1970s at Expo Steam, when it was demonstrating direct ploughing.

The oldest surviving Mann has a long and interesting history. Works no. 881 was completed as a tractor in 1914 for the War Department and used for gun haulage in France. After the war it passed into the ownership of Fylde Council, and later went to Isaac Balls of Southport where it was used as a roller. It was rebuilt into a wagon a few years ago.

This 5 ton Mann wagon was built in 1916 as works no. 1120 and was supplied new to T. Frampton, haulage contractor of Farnham. Most of its work was furniture haulage and removals. It was rescued for preservation in 1960 and is now part of a collection of steam wagons.

Marshall Sons & Co. Ltd
Britannia Iron Works, Gainsborough, Lincs.

This north Lincolnshire company is probably best known for its sturdy traction engines, produced in large numbers for both the home and overseas markets. They were, of course, also involved with many other products, both steam and internal combustion engines. Several hundred steam engines have survived, including a great many tractions. Marshall's offered single-cylinder and compound designs in 5, 6, 7 and 8 nhp. The earliest survivor is a single-cylinder 6 nhp engine, no. 14242 *Victoria, Empress of India*, completed in September 1886 and now to be found at Brighton Engineerium. The youngest survivor is no. 87087, a 7 nhp compound with overhead slide valve built in 1933 – at a time when sales of traction engines had fallen away dramatically owing to the ever-increasing number of diesel tractors on the market.

Several Marshall traction engines originally sold to owners overseas have returned home for preservation, most in derelict condition. One road locomotive to return from Australia was no. 52962 *Britannia*, a three-speed slide-valve compound 8 nhp completed in October 1909 and supplied to R.C. Scrutton & Co. Ltd of Sydney. The engine required a full rebuild and this was completed in time for the Marshall to make its rally debut in 1991. Since then it has appeared at events over a wide area.

There are a few surviving tractors built by Marshall's and others which started life as road-rollers. The first were of a single-cylinder design, but this was fairly shortlived; although it was kept on for a while in roller form, it was not long before a compound tractor appeared and again this was used as the basis for a roller.

Rollers were a very important part of the company's business, with one of the most successful being the 'S' class, available in 6–16 ton sizes. A large number of these have survived, and examples of the roller were still working commercially into the early 1960s. The youngest survivor of this class is no. 89549, built in 1944, a 12 ton compound piston-valve engine. In the 1930s new road surfaces were coming into use which required easily manoeuvrable, instant reverse rollers that did not dwell and sink into the surface.

Marshall's also introduced a tandem vertical boiler model. Two of these have survived and one of them is occasionally seen at events: no. 87125 is a 5 nhp 10 ton design completed in July 1933. This engine was supplied to Norwich Corporation and is thought to have last worked during the war on airfield construction. Over the following years it became derelict before being rescued for preservation. Only seven of this type were built, several of them going overseas. Another design was the 'Universal', quick reverse engines with no flywheel. Four of this type survive including the last one built, no. 87635, which was completed in June 1935. This was sold new to West Sussex County Council, becoming their Fleet no. 49; it worked until the mid-1960s before being sold for preservation.

With so many Marshall traction engines in preservation they are common at rallies. Considerable interest was aroused at Carrington rally held in May 1997 with the first public appearance of Marshall light traction no. 53048, an engine which spent its working life in South Africa and returned to Britain in 1996. Its owner Robert Coles purchased it over the telephone! This Marshall has several very different features from those built for the home market: it is fitted with a disc crank, friction clutch, steam dome, feed water heater and Pickering governors. In the years prior to its return it had received boiler work at a South African railway workshop.

This magnificent Marshall, works no. 52962 *Britannia*, spent its working life in Australia. Built in 1909, it was exported to R.C. Scrutton, the Marshall's agent in Sydney. Very little is known of its early history until it entered preservation in 1960. Robert Coles also purchased this fine engine over the telephone and arranged its return to this country. Since then it has undergone an extensive rebuild and now appears at events all over the country.

The Marshall 6 nhp, a light traction engine, has a very unusual appearance. No. 53048 was built in 1909 and exported to E.F. Ford, Marshall's agent in Pietermaritzburg, South Africa. It is seen here, resplendent in green livery, making its first public appearance at Carrington on 25 May 1997, just twelve months after returning to Britain. Built to burn wood or straw, it has a number of interesting features including disc crank, friction clutch, steam dome, feed water heater and Pickering governors.

This splendid Marshall 8 nhp single-cylinder traction engine, no. 37823 *Old Ned*, was completed in 1901 and exported to Tasmania where it was used on threshing, stone-crushing and road haulage. The engine returned to Britain in pieces in 1991, since when it has undergone an extensive rebuild, including new boiler barrel and firebox, gears, axle, bearings and tender, making it virtually a new engine. The Marshall is named after its original Tasmanian owner who worked with it for fifty years.

Only a few genuine tractors built by Marshall's are in preservation, since some of those we see today started life as road-rollers. This fine example of the company's 4 nhp 5 ton design was completed in November 1920 as works no. 73900. After exhibition at the Smithfield show the following month it was delivered to its new owners, Norfolk County Council. It now carries the name *Jubilee* and is thought to be one of two surviving tractors fitted with the Marshall radial valve gear.

Marshall 7 nhp single-cylinder slide-valve engine, works no. 49725 *Old Nick*, is preserved at Colchester. It is a much travelled engine in preservation, appearing at events over a wide area. This engine started life in 1908 in the ownership of the Oxford Steam Plough Company, later known as John Allen & Sons Ltd, and it still carries a plate to that effect. Its final years in commercial life were spent in Yorkshire.

Marshall no. 49222 used to be part of the collection owned by the late Tom Paisley of Holywell. It is an 8 nhp single-cylinder slide-valve engine and is fitted with a feed water heater which can be clearly seen in this picture. The engine was previously in the ownership of T. Stamp of Market Rasen, Lincolnshire. Some work was done in the early days at Holywell before the auction sale held in October 1980.

This very unusual Marshall tandem vertical boiler roller, no. 87125 built in 1933, is a 10 ton twin-cylinder roller with steam-powered steering and instant reverse. Only seven of this type were produced, five of which were exported. The roller's first owner was Norwich City Council, where it became Fleet no. 8; by the mid-1940s it had moved on to Ben Jordon of Cottishall where it remained until purchased for preservation. It is thought to have been little used after the Second World War.

There are only a small number of Marshall 'Universal' rollers still in existence. Works no. 87260 *Rolling On* was completed in February 1934 and was owned by West Riding County Council, being Fleet no. 63. The Marshall is pictured here a long way from its home at Boston, while it was taking part in the 1991 Marshall display at the Great Dorset Steam Fair.

This Marshall 4 nhp 8 ton S class roller, no. 76116, is a compound with piston valves and was the first to be fitted with Marshall's patent valve gearing. It was completed in February 1923, going new to Weston-super-Mare Council and later moving to a contractor in Bath before being purchased for restoration. This superbly preserved example of a neat Marshall design is seen here at an event in Louth, Lincolnshire.

John & Henry McLaren Ltd
Midland Engine Works, Leeds

This is another long-established Leeds company, commencing in 1876. Luckily a variety of the engines built there have survived. Like most of the large companies, McLaren's had both home and overseas markets, in addition supplying road engines and tractions of the War Office for use in the Boer War as well as haulage engines for the First World War. Over the years export destinations included Australia, South Africa, New Zealand and Zanzibar.

Despite the intense competition the company faced from its neighbour Fowler's, McLaren's became involved with the ploughing engines market. Steam was, of course, the principal power on farms in the early years of the twentieth century. Two examples have survived: no. 1514 *Avis* completed in August 1918, a 12 nhp design; and no. 1552 *Hero* completed in March 1919. This engine was working in Somerset until 1960 when it was finally laid aside. It soon deteriorated but fortunately it was rescued for preservation and restored. Despite being based in Cornwall, this engine has been seen at numerous events over the last thirty years, particularly at the Great Dorset. Ploughing engines were also exported, a number being sent to Hungary.

McLaren's was also very much involved with the road locomotive market, and the earliest survivor in Britain is a 6 nhp which returned home from New Zealand. Another engine which spent most of its working life overseas, in this case in Australia, was the 10 nhp no. 1332 built in 1912. It was originally built for the War Department and was exported after the First World War, now carrying the name *Gigantic*.

The 8 nhp three-speed no. 1421 *Captain Scott* was supplied to an owner at Conisborough, Yorkshire. With the outbreak of the First World War it was soon commandeered, eventually finding itself working on the construction of Cranwell aerodrome. Its final commercial work was on agricultural duties, and it eventually became derelict.

McLaren's 10 nhp design was found to be suitable for gun haulage, and fifty-five were built for this, hauling 49 mm guns. Most were sent overseas, but one that was not was no. 1652 *Boadicea* completed in January 1919. Passing into private hands, this engine worked on general haulage. In due course it was purchased by Edwin Corrigan and returned to McLaren's works for conversion to full showman's specification and renamed *Gigantic*. This was not a success as the engine soon proved to be too heavy for showland work. Another change of owner resulted in the McLaren returning to heavy haulage, this time hauling boilers for Shaw & Gaskell of Hull. Eventually it ended up on fenland dredging, being laid aside in 1958. Happily this engine did not suffer the indignity of becoming derelict before being rescued and its next owner was the late Steve Neville who purchased it and steamed it home. The McLaren soon became a familiar sight in the summer months steaming to and from events, often travelling a considerable distance from its Saffron Walden base.

Another 10 nhp engine which started life with the War Department on gun haulage was no. 1623 *Goliath*, which was completed in June 1918. It was sold to Pat Collins of Walsall after the war and converted to full showman's specification. This engine is now part of a collection based in Cheshire and has been seen at numerous events throughout the country. Over the years twenty-six McLarens have worked on the fairgrounds; some, such as *Lucky Durham*, were initially built for showmen, while others, such as *Goliath*, were converted during their working lives.

After the War many of these ex-War Department engines were sold off through surplus sales. At one time Mornement & Ray Ltd owned six of the 10 nhp engines (or 'Big Macs' as they were known), as well as several ex-WD Fowlers in its ownership. The

McLarens were converted for dredging work and employed in eastern England, three of them later working in Somerset in the early 1940s. Sadly none of these six engines survived.

The showman 8 nhp road locomotive no. 1713 *The Banshee* was completed in January 1922. It worked as a crane engine for Northampton Corporation and then moved to Ireland until a few years ago. Conversion to showman's specification took place during preservation.

There are twenty examples of the company's traction engine designs in preservation including both singles and compounds, the latter all 5 nhp engines, whereas the singles include 6, 7, and 8 nhp engines. All have slide valves. There is also a 6 nhp single-cylinder 5 ton roller built in 1908, and at one stage the company offered a range of rollers from 6 to 20 tons.

McLaren's also built tractors of which three have survived. No. 1413 *May Queen* was completed in December 1913, *Pamir* no. 1663 in July 1919 and the last one, no. 1837 *Bluebell*, not until April 1936. The latter was supplied to Acre Iron Works at Alton, Hants, for road haulage. This 4 nhp 5 ton compound is a familiar sight at events held in eastern England.

McLaren's of Leeds supplied a number of powerful 10 nhp road locomotives to the War Department during the First World War for gun haulage in France. No. 1623 completed in June 1918 was one of these. It was later purchased by Pat Collins of Walsall and converted to showman's specification. In later years it was on display at Alton Towers Amusement Park. The engine is now preserved in Cheshire and carries the name *Goliath*.

During the early days of the preservation movement this McLaren, no. 1652 *Boadicea*, was a familiar sight on the roads during the summer months travelling to and from events with its owner, the late Steve Neville, shown here in 1963. The 10 nhp was among the batch built for the War Department but it was not completed until January 1919, after the war had finished. It was then used on heavy haulage work and later purchased by Edwin Corrigan and converted to full showman's specification but it was found to be too heavy and was soon sold to Shaw & Gaskell of Hull for hauling boilers. It ended its working life dredging in East Anglia.

McLaren's was well known for its road locomotives. This 8 nhp compound three-speed engine, no. 1421 *Captain Scott*, was completed in May 1913 and supplied to Wakefields of Conisborough where it was employed on stone haulage. At the outbreak of the First World War in 1914 there was a need for engines of various types and the McLaren was commandeered for use on airfield construction in Lincolnshire. It then worked in Yorkshire and later at Chesterfield, at the latter on haulage and agricultural work, before being laid aside in 1945. It was an early engine on the rally scene but as absent for a number of years, returning in 1993.

This 10 nhp McLaren was originally ordered by the War Department but instead it was shipped out to Australia where it spent its entire working life, returning to Britain in the early 1980s. Works no. 1332 *Gigantic*, a three-speed compound engine, was completed in 1912. Notice the round coal bunkers. This massive engine is currently undergoing a complete overhaul.

This engine is one of the oldest McLaren traction engines to survive. Works no. 127 *The Little Wonder* was completed in August 1882, a single-cylinder 8 nhp design. For many years it was preserved in Bedfordshire, where this picture was taken. Note the set of spuds at the front. The oldest surviving McLaren traction was built in 1879.

There are twenty McLaren traction engines in preservation in the British Isles, all built between 1879 and 1918. The majority are single-cylinder designs and 6 nhp no. 435 *Himself*, built in 1892, is one of these. This engine was supplied new to an owner in Tipperary, Ireland, but after passing through several hands it ended up derelict.

One of the best-preserved examples of the McLaren traction engines is no. 757 *Loyalty*, built in 1904. This engine spent its working life in Co. Meath, Ireland, being supplied via a Dublin agent. It was later employed as a heavy roller. It was fitted with a new firebox at the GNR(I) railway workshops in the early 1940s, returning to Britain in the late 1960s. After changing hands it has now been restored to its original specifications.

Two McLaren ploughing engines survive in the British Isles, a 12 nhp and this one, 16 nhp no. 1552 *Hero*, built in 1919. This engine finished its working life at Langport, Somerset, in 1960. When rescued for preservation it was in a poor condition and the winding drum was missing, but this fine McLaren has now been on the rally fields for over thirty years, sometimes travelling far from its base in Cornwall.

The youngest McLaren engine surviving in Britain is the 4 nhp compound tractor no. 1837 *Bluebell*, completed in April 1936. Its commercial life commenced with timber haulage in Wiltshire and ended on Southampton Docks, but it has spent more time in preservation than it did at work.

Ransomes, Sims & Jefferies Ltd
Orwell Works, Ipswich

This is another East Anglian company with a high reputation for its engines. Originally trading as Ransomes, Sims & Head, it changed in 1881 to Ransomes Head & Jefferies and just three years later to the above company name. A considerable number of engines built by Ransomes have survived. Most are tractions or portables, the latter including examples built as late as 1943. There are also quite a number of both types in preservation in Ireland. One single-cylinder traction, no. 27000 built in 1916, was for a number of years to be seen at East Anglian events until it was sold to a museum in Rimini, Italy. This engine carried an EW registration plate, indicating that it originated in Huntingdonshire.

The single-cylinder slide-valve crane engine, no. 31066, was completed in April 1920. The crane jib is mounted around the chimney and is capable of a maximum 5 ton lift. This interesting example spent its working life as the works crane engine, ending up at Hardwick's scrapyard, Ewell. Luckily it was rescued for preservation and after several owners is now preserved in Hampshire, and on occasions it can be seen in action using its crane.

There are six tractors in preservation, five in England and one in Ireland. The oldest is no. 23266, built in July 1910. A compound slide-valve example, it was at one time in preservation in East Anglia and attended some of the early rallies in the area. It was also used for demonstrations and visited shows over a wide area.

Also used as a show engine, in this case for six years, was no. 36220. Completed in May 1920 as no. 31109, it was subsequently allocated several different works numbers, the one it presently carries being the one it carried at the Highland Show in 1925. It was sold the following year, having two owners during its working life.

Ransomes did try to break into the showman's engine market, but fierce competition from Burrell's in the neighbouring county meant that their efforts met with little success and only a few were constructed. They were never very popular. Nevertheless, Ransomes built up a good home and overseas business and a number of their engines, mostly portables, survive in various continental countries.

Only six examples of the Ransomes, Sims & Jefferies steam tractors survive, five in Britain and one in Ireland. This example, no. 39149, completed in October 1928, is the youngest. It is a 4 nhp compound slide-valve engine weighing 5 tons. Ransomes faced major competition from Garrett's of Leiston, well known for its popular 4CD design. This engine, like so many others, laid aside for over twenty-five years, eventually became derelict before being rescued in the 1970s.

For six years this Ransomes tractor was the show engine. Built in 1920, it toured many major agricultural shows and received a new works number each year, this process coming to an end at the Highland Show in 1925. It was sold in 1926 as no. 36220. It is a 4 nhp compound tractor, seen here resplendent in smart green livery, having had a complete rebuild in the late 1980s.

This splendid example of the Ransomes 7 nhp single-cylinder slide-valve design, works no. 30004, was built in 1919. It ended up derelict in a scrapyard from where it was rescued for preservation. Engines built by Ransomes, Sims & Jefferies were highly regarded in farming circles both at home and overseas and a considerable number have survived into preservation.

This engine always attracts attention wherever it goes. The 6 nhp single-cylinder slide-valve crane engine no. 31066 *Hooky* was built in 1920. It spent its working life as the yard engine, and was used to move completed engines, castings and supplies as necessary. It ended up at Hardwick's of Ewell. The engine has had several owners in preservation, receiving a new firebox and boiler barrel in the early 1990s. It has been superbly restored and is often seen giving demonstrations in various parts of the country.

Robey & Co. Ltd
Globe Works, Lincoln

Lincolnshire also had a long history of steam engine building, with four major companies based in Lincoln itself and Marshall's not many miles away. One of these Lincoln companies was Robey & Co. Ltd. Its first agricultural engine appeared in 1862, and over the years the company developed a range of single-cylinder and compound engines, a few examples of which have survived into preservation. One of these is no. 29330, a 6 nhp three-speed compound with overhead slide valves completed in June 1910. This engine was supplied new to F.B. Gibbons & Sons of Baston near Peterborough, principally for road haulage work but by the 1920s it was more often used for threshing. This grand old engine is still owned by the company and attends rallies over a wide area, presenting a fine sight with its overall 'Lincolnshire'-type canopy and smart brown livery.

For the all-important tractor market Robey's produced a 4 nhp model, several examples of which have survived. The earliest is no. 33957 which was built in 1915 and supplied new to Fisher & Co. of Tamworth, with whom it remained for twenty-two years before moving to Crowman & Son of Leicester. It is currently preserved in Lincolnshire. No. 41492, completed in January 1924, was supplied new to the RASC. It will be very familiar to many readers in its showman's tractor form.

Very different in appearance were the company's 'Express' tractors. Only nine were built of this compound piston-valve design weighing 7 tons. Two still survive in the

British Isles, no. 43165 completed in January 1927 and no. 43388 of February 1929. At the time of writing both are in preservation in Devon.

The road locomotive market was also catered for, the company producing both single-cylinder and compound designs available in 6, 7, 8 and 10 nhp power outputs. Sadly none of these has survived. Another unusual design produced by Robey's was the tandem roller for the road construction industry. It was a compound piston-valve engine with stayless circular 'Thimble' fireboxes. Eight tandems have survived, along with two of the Tri tandems. One of the tandems, no. 42520 *Barkus*, built in 1925, is part of the Bressingham Steam Museum collection. Two rollers of more conventional design survive. No. 32387 is a compound slide-valve 10 ton model built in 1913 and currently with the Robey Trust Museum. No. 41113 is a single-cylinder 12.5 ton model built in 1923 and now preserved in Ireland.

Until 1996 there was only one complete working example of the wagons built by Robey to be found in the British Isles. No. 42567 was built in 1925 and supplied to Highways Colloidal Ltd, complete with a Hines patent road dryer and tar spraying apparatus. It was rescued for preservation from a scrapyard at Amersham. But at the 1996 Carrington rally a second Robey steam wagon, no. 42522 built in 1926, made its debut. This has a very interesting history and has been the subject of a long and involved restoration project. The wagon was supplied new to William Gossage & Sons Ltd, soap and chemical manufacturers of Widnes, Lancashire, for use as an articulated tanker. Gossage's also operated two other Robey wagons of the platform type. The wagon's engine and boiler eventually turned up in a tandem roller in the ownership of Bournemouth Corporation. The extensive rebuilding project took seven years and included the fitting of a new chassis, body, cab and Ackerman steering. Both surviving examples of the Robey wagons are in preservation in Lincolnshire. None of the earlier vertical boiler undertypes survives.

The fine example of the Robey 6 nhp compound design is a three-speed engine with overhead slide valves. This example has been with the same family since new in 1910, over the years being used on threshing and other agricultural work as well as stone-crushing. The engine is owned by F.B. Gibbons & Sons Ltd and it was seen on the rally fields with the same driver for fifty years in both working and preservation days.

This is Robey showman's tractor no. 41492, a 4 nhp engine completed in January 1924. It was originally supplied to RASC and was later employed on timber haulage. When laid aside it became buried under sawdust but was saved for preservation and converted to showman's specification.

This picture of Robey Tri tandem roller no. 44083 was taken in the mid-1960s. Only two of this type exist. This two-speed double-crank compound with stayless circular 'Thimble' firebox was completed in May 1930 and converted to Tri tandem in the mid-1930s. In later years the Robey was owned by Wirksworth Quarries Ltd of Bury St Edmunds, working at Luton airport and the Grantham by-pass until the late 1960s, being acquired for preservation five years later.

The Robey 'Express' tractor was a rather unconventional design. Only nine were built and fortunately two have survived. No. 43388 *Deeside Knight* was built in 1929. It is a 4 nhp compound piston-valve chain-drive engine with circular firebox. Coal and water supplies were stored behind the driver. It is pictured here in the 1970s in the ownership of the late Tom Varley. Both examples are currently preserved in the west country. This tractor's last owner was W. Smith Sawmills of Fakenham, Norfolk.

The superb restoration of this Robey overtype steam wagon was completed in 1996. This is the second of the Robey wagons to survive in the British Isles. Both are currently in Lincolnshire, the county in which they were built. No. 42522 was completed in 1926 and supplied new as an articulated tanker to William Gossage & Sons Ltd, soap and chemical manufacturers of Widnes. This company operated three wagons, two of which were Robeys. The engine and boiler were later used in a tandem roller owned by Bournemouth Corporation, which was purchased by Alan Rundle in 1988. Rebuilding included a new chassis, body, cab and Ackerman steering. The wagon is fitted with a stayless piston type boiler and piston valves.

Robinson & Auden Ltd
The Vale of White Horse Foundry, Wantage

The original company, Gibbons & Robinson, built seven traction engines, one of which has survived. In 1891 it changed into Robinson & Auden, and became a limited company on 23 May 1894. The Gibbons & Robinson engine no. 959 is an 8 nhp single-cylinder traction completed in June 1891 and supplied new to Thomas Swain of Narrington, Wiltshire. Its later history is uncertain, but it is known that its last owner was Mr F. Williams of Preston on Wye in 1941 and it passed into preservation in 1960.

Only one traction engine built by Robinson & Auden survives. Completed in July 1900 as works no. 1376, it is a 6 nhp single-cylinder slide-valve design. Its early history is also somewhat sketchy but it is known to have been in the ownership of Mr A. Izard in 1916 and of Mr E.J. Garlick of Winchcombe in 1948. In 1965 it passed to the late Tom Paisley in a derelict condition. Many new parts and a firebox were required to get this interesting engine back in steam. There are also four Robinson & Auden portable engines in preservation built between 1892 and 1894.

In 1900 the company name changed again, this time becoming the Wantage Engineering Co. Ltd. Two traction engines from this period survive. The oldest is an 8 nhp single-cylinder slide-valve engine completed in December 1900 and the other is a 7 nhp single-cylinder slide-valve design completed in April 1908.

Only one traction engine built by Robinson & Auden survives. No. 1376, completed on 31 July 1900, is a 6 nhp single-cylinder two-speed design. This general purpose traction had several owners during its working life, the last being E.J. Garlick of Winchcombe. It was purchased derelict in 1965 for preservation. Restoration required a new firebox, and several parts for which new patterns had to be made. In preservation it acquired the name *Little Buttercup* after one of the principal characters in a Gilbert & Sullivan operetta.

Another unique example is this Gibbons & Robinson engine, no. 959 of June 1891. An 8 nhp single-cylinder design, it was the last of seven built under this name. This engine originally worked in Wiltshire but by the late 1920s it had moved to Hereford before passing to its final owner, F. Williams of Preston on Wye who used it until the early 1940s.

Ruston & Hornsby Ltd
Sheaf Iron Works, Lincoln

The history of this company is somewhat complicated. It is the result of the amalgamation of two long-established engine building companies. On 11 September 1918 Richard Hornsby & Sons Ltd of Grantham and Ruston Proctor & Co. Ltd of Lincoln became Ruston & Hornsby Ltd. There are a few surviving engines built by Richard Hornsby & Sons, mostly portables but also three traction engines, all 8 nhp singles built between 1889 and 1892. Ruston Proctor & Co. Ltd have a wider range in preservation in the British Isles, including 5, 7, and 8 nhp traction engines, the oldest being a 7 nhp single-cylinder type SH built in 1907. In addition there are five steamrollers, two of which are SR type of 3 and 6 nhp, 6 and 10 tons respectively. The other three are type SCR. There are also a number of portable engines and a 4 nhp tractor, no. 52329 built in 1918 as type SCD.

One of the traction engines is no. 35501 *The Muddler*, an 8 nhp single-cylinder slide-valve engine built in 1908. This engine is well known in the eastern counties, travelling to and from events under its own steam. It was sold new to Uriah Spratt of

Thornton near Horncastle in Lincolnshire and used principally for road haulage work. It moved to a new owner in the same county in 1921 and was then mainly used for threshing. *The Muddler* has been with its present owner for many years, during which time it has undertaken some considerable journeys clocking up a hefty mileage in the process.

Ruston Proctor no. 51737, a 5 nhp single-speed type SP single slide-valve engine, was built for the colonial market but never sent. In the company's catalogue a class SA traction engine was offered in 6 to 12 nhp with a firebox for burning straw and other refuse material. These single-speed engines boasted improved waterlift, a large firebox and a large straw carrier.

The surviving engines built by Ruston & Hornsby Ltd consist of a number of portables and nine tractions. The youngest, no. 169167 *Trevithick* built in 1933, is one of the SH 'heavy pattern', as the company described it. Rollers are represented by ten examples of type SR and SCR, with five 'Lincoln Imp' tractors completing the list.

This Ruston Proctor type SH single-cylinder slide-valve 7 nhp engine has been on the rally scene for thirty years. Works no. 34987 *Rusty* was built in 1908. After a long working life it was laid aside and eventually sold for scrap. It is one of the oldest examples of this company's traction engines to survive in the British Isles.

This fine Ruston Proctor 8 nhp traction engine is no. 35501 *The Muddler*, which travels considerable distances under its own steam to and from events. Built in 1908, it was supplied to Uriah Spratt of Thornton near Horncastle in Lincolnshire and was used on road haulage. The engine is fitted with belly tanks. In the early 1920s it passed to Epton's of New Bolingbroke and was used principally for threshing work.

Another picture from the archives, taken at Raynham Day in 1962. Ruston & Hornsby 6 nhp no. 113043 *Oliver*, a type SH single-cylinder slide-valve engine, was built in 1920. It was supplied new to W. Godfrey of Icketon and used for timber hauling and sawing work, later passing into the ownership of Coxalls, threshing contractors near Cambridge. In 1924 it moved to its last commercial owner, C.R. Pumfrey of Duxford, and it worked until the late 1940s when it was sold for scrap. It was rescued shortly afterwards and is now a regular sight at rallies.

Ruston & Hornsby completed this 7 nhp type SH single-cylinder slide-valve engine, works no. 122160, in May 1923. Examples of this design survive in 5, 6 and 7 nhp models, the youngest of which was built in 1933 at a time when the demand for traction engines was falling off dramatically.

Only ten steamrollers built by Ruston & Hornsby survive in the British Isles. No. 149813 *Success*, a 6 nhp type SR 10 ton model, was completed in March 1928 and supplied by Ransomes Sims & Jefferies to Claytons, contractors based at Cottishall. Five years later it moved to Plumbly & Gaze, remaining with them until 1962 when it went straight into preservation.

The 'Lincoln Imp' steam tractor was Ruston & Hornsby's design for the important tractor market. This is 4 nhp no. 52573 *Lucifer*, completed in November 1918. It was built for the War Department but as the war had just finished it was retained as the works engine, later being sold to an owner on the Isle of Man and used on the docks. It returned to the mainland in 1929 and was converted to a roller. Restoration to a tractor took place in the 1960s.

Sentinel (Shrewsbury) Ltd
Shrewsbury, Shropshire

Steam wagons built by this company fall into four types: the Standard, Super, DG and S series. The latter were fast efficient wagons ahead of their time when they were introduced in the early 1930s. The company also built tractors and many steam railway locomotives for main line and industrial use, as well as steam railcars for use on secondary and branch lines.

The earliest Sentinel was the 'Standard' design produced between 1906 and 1923. A considerable number of these were supplied to the War Department: the army received 200 6 tonners for use in France, while more than 115 were supplied to the Admiralty and Air Ministry. After the war these wagons were among the vast number of surplus vehicles on sale, seriously depressing the new wagon market for a considerable time. Large and small transport operations seized the opportunity to take advantage of these cheap vehicles.

The 'Standards' offered some protection for the driver and mate in so much as they had a cab roof, but they were open at the front and sides. Several wagons of this type have survived, mainly owing to their use by Brown Bayley Steels of Sheffield where some were still working in the late 1960s. They were used for transporting hot metal to the rolling mills and slag to the tips. Some of the Sentinels used by the company spent their entire working lives on this work. One of the survivors is no. 1488, built in 1917 and supplied new to Brown Bayley, becoming their fleet No. 8. It was purchased in the 1960s by Bradford Industrial Museum and restored. In the late 1960s it moved to the Bass Museum at Burton-on-Trent and is occasionally seen at events.

In 1923 the prototype 'Super' appeared. Improvements included a more weatherproof cab, although solid rubber tyres were still fitted. The design followed the basic principle of the earlier Sentinels, having a vertical boiler, undermounted engine and separate chain drives to each rear wheel. Development was constantly taking place, and in the late 1920s the 'DG' series appeared. They were still chain driven, but were more powerful units operating at 275 psi, and available initially in four- or six-wheel designs. In September 1930 the first eight-wheeler was introduced. It was a design considerably before its time. Eight were built new and a further eight were converted from six-wheel DG wagons. The 'DG' series remained in production for approximately seven years. Examples of the 'DG4' and 'DG6' survive but there are no 'DG8s'.

In 1933 the final Sentinel design was introduced: the 'S' series. These were shaft driven, and boasted numerous improvements such as modern cabs, sliding windows, electric wipers and lighting, and pneumatic tyres. They were economical vehicles capable of 60 mph fully loaded, which compared very favourably with other vehicles of the day. Four- and six-wheel examples have survived plus one 'S8', no. 9105 built in 1934. Initially the works demonstration wagon, this was later to spend much of its working life hauling steel plate from South Wales to the Ford works at Dagenham. When rescued for preservation all that remained was a derelict chassis.

Several of the surviving Sentinels enjoyed a brief moment of glory when they were put back into service during the Suez oil crisis. Indeed if this had not been the case we would be without several of the Sentinels and Fodens which we see in action today. The record for long service must go to DG4 no. 8122, completed in December 1929, which was supplied to A.E. Knox of Erdington. The wagon spent its early years hauling bricks and minerals. In 1943 it changed hands and was converted to use as a tar sprayer in Cheshire. During 1974 it was sold to an owner in North Wales and it was not laid up until the early 1980s. On 26 April 1997 it was entered in the Chilford Hall sale, complete as it last worked with 1,350 gallon tank, spray bar and hand lance, the tar equipment being operated by a single-cylinder steam pump. This Sentinel has now passed into preservation after a long working life. Others ended their days as tar sprayers.

Sentinel's also developed tractor designs for both the home and overseas markets. One which was to become a familiar sight at events in the 1960s and 1970s was 'Super' no. 5644 *The Elephant*. Built in 1924, it was supplied new to the Teignmouth Quarry Co. Ltd and was used for many years shunting wagons on the docks. During the late 1980s it was sold to an enthusiast in Holland but it has since returned to this country. Sentinel's also produced a small number of timber tractors, which were expensive units when new. This design has a single boiler working two engines, one for propulsion, the other driving a winch. Four of these timber tractors have survived into preservation. One of these is no. 8756 *Brutus*, a DG 4 built in 1933. *Brutus* can be seen on display at Bressingham Steam Museum. No. 8777 *Old*

Bill was also built the same year, and no. 9097 was constructed in 1934 and supplied to A. Wootton & Sons of Cannock, Staffordshire. The fourth is currently in Holland

Due to the massive increase in road tax for steam wagons in the 1930 act many were withdrawn from service and a number were converted to tractors for short haul work. Conversions were done at the Sentinel Service Garage in Vauxhall Road, Liverpool, and only three so converted have survived. One of these is 'Super' no. 5558, built in 1924 and supplied new to Hodgesons Kingston Brewery. After conversion the wagon was used by Symonds, Hunt and Montgomery, and was later to change owners. During this time it often travelled from Birkenhead to Liverpool docks, and continued in use until 1962, becoming the last Sentinel to work in the Liverpool area.

Over the years a number of Sentinel wagons once in preservation in Britain have gone to enthusiasts overseas. No. 8992, an S4 built in 1934 and fitted with tanker body, has gone to Australia, as has no. 9310 built in 1937. Three S series examples have gone to the United States together with tractor no. 7527; wagon no. 8827 has gone to Holland and 'Standard' no. 3899 to Sweden. Nevertheless we still have almost one hundred wagons and tractors in the British Isles.

This 'Standard' design Sentinel wagon, works no. 1488, was built in 1917 and supplied new to Brown Bayley Steelworks at Sheffield, becoming fleet No. 8. This company operated several wagons to transport hot metals to the mill, remove waste and perform various other duties, some of them remaining in service until the early 1970s. *No. 1*, as it is known, was restored and housed at the Bradford Industrial Museum for a number of years before moving on to the Bass Museum, Burton-on-Trent, in the late 1960s.

Sentinel DG6 no. 8213 was completed in May 1930, becoming Britain's first mobile concrete-mixer in the ownership of the British Steel Piling Co. of Vauxhall, London. The idea proved to be too ambitious for its day and the Sentinel was left derelict until the outbreak of the war. It then passed to Willments of Twickenham who used it as a stationary mixer on government sites. For a short time in its early days of preservation it appeared with the mixer body before this dropside body was fitted.

Sentinel no. 8381 was built in 1930 and is pictured here complete with trailer at Pickering. Formerly part of the Holywell collection, this wagon was the only item not included in the sale in 1980. Instead it was moved to a Glasgow timber yard where it remained for several years. Restoration to working order took over two years, and since then it has been seen at events over a wide area.

This Sentinel 'Super' design no. 7591 had several owners, having been supplied new in 1928 to George Senior & Sons Ltd of Sheffield, and later moving to Pashley & Trickett. Its final move was to Brown Bayley Steelworks where it joined the fleet of 'Standards' already there.

This fine example of the Sentinel 'Super', no. 5471, was completed in 1924 and sold new to Fred Dyke of Farnham. It was later sold on to F. Goymer & Sons of Barking, Essex, before going to its final owner, James & Sons, grain merchants of Bermondsey. Eventually the wagon ended up in J.W. Hardwicks scrapyard from where it was rescued for preservation. It is currently based in Northern Ireland.

On 26 April 1997 the Sentinel DG4 tar spraying wagon finally made it into preservation at the Chilford Hall sale. Works no. 8122 was completed as a wagon in December 1929 and supplied new to A.E. Knox of Erdington, spending its early days on brick haulage. Later it was employed on mineral haulage. In 1943 it was converted into a tar spraying wagon and in 1974 it was purchased by Ewan Jones to work on road and pathway construction in North Wales before being laid up in the early 1980s. It is believed that this example was the last to work commercially in the UK. The wagon was sold complete with 1,350 gallon tank, a single-cylinder steam pump, spray bar and hand lance, exactly as it finished work.

Sentinel was a progressive company and its final steam wagon design, the 'S' series, was well ahead of its time. This example, no. 8448, was an experimental vehicle, a prototype for the 'S' series, which was built in 1930. It was fitted with steam brakes on all wheels. In 1931 it passed into the ownership of the Grieve Haulage Co. of Birkenhead who used it for six years, often with a trailer. It has been in preservation for over forty years, attending events over a wide area.

The majority of the 'S' series Sentinel wagons in preservation are four-wheel models, but there are also five six-wheelers including this one, no. 8821, built in July 1933 and pictured here in Tarmac Limited livery at a Bishop's Castle rally a few years ago. There is also one surviving example of the S8 eight-wheel design.

Sentinel S4s were fast efficient vehicles incorporating many new features, such as pneumatic tyres, electric lighting and windscreen wipers. Completed in April 1934, no. 9016 was supplied to E. & S. Shadrack Ltd, coal and coke merchants operating in London. In due course it passed to new owners Wingham Engineers who used it until 1950.

Only a few of the powerful Sentinel timber tractors were built, four of which have survived into preservation. No. 9097 is a DG4 model completed in October 1934 and supplied to A. Woolton & Sons of Cannock, Staffordshire, later passing into the ownership of C. James & Son of Kingswinford. The tractor has a 120 bhp double-geared engine for traction with a separate 40 hp unit for operating the winch mounted at the rear. Pneumatic tyres are also fitted. Over the years this tractor has had several owners in preservation.

Quite a number of Sentinel wagons were converted to tractors and sadly all but three have been scrapped. 'Super' no. 5558, built in 1924, started life delivering beer around London for its owners Hodgesons Brewery of Kingston upon Thames; after ten years it moved on to Symonds, Hunt & Montgomery Ltd in Liverpool. In the early 1930s it was sent to the Sentinel service garage in Liverpool for conversion to a tractor. It was still at work until 1962 in the Liverpool area in the ownership of Criddle & Co.

For many years this Sentinel 'Super' tractor was a familiar sight shunting railway wagons on the Teignmouth Docks, a duty it performed until the early 1960s. The tractor was one of two originally ordered by Jacks, Sentinel's agent in Calcutta, but no. 5644 *The Elephant* was not sent out. After a period of time it was sold to the Teignmouth Quay Co. where it remained until rescued for preservation. Since then it has had several owners including one at Kroonmennie in Holland. It is now back in Britain.

This Sentinel timber tractor is on display at Bressingham Steam Museum. Works no. 8756 *Brutus*, a DG4, was built in 1933, and has two engines. These powerful timber tractors were very expensive to buy, and so only a few were made. This example was originally supplied to T. Place & Sons Ltd of Northallerton, but subsequently had several other owners during its working life. Despite its size the Sentinel is capable of 35 mph.

W. Tasker & Sons Ltd
Waterloo Ironworks, Andover, Hampshire

Mention the name Tasker to steam enthusiasts and most will immediately think of the 'Little Giant' tractor, although this was far from being the company's only product. Tasker's also made tractions, rollers, wagons and portable engines.

The oldest surviving Tasker traction engine, no. 352 of 1893, is now in the care of the Hampshire County Council Museum Service together with several other engines built by this company. Of the four other surviving tractors, all C types, three are in private hands. Only a handful of Tasker road-rollers survive, one which can occasionally be seen at events. This is no. 1933, a C class 6 nhp single-cylinder slide-valve engine weighing 10 tons, and also in the care of the Museum Service. This was the last example built by the company and spent its working life with Watson & Haig.

A few years ago the restoration of the sole surviving Tasker wagon in the British Isles was completed. This 5 ton tipper, no. 1915 of 1924, was supplied new to W.J. King of Bishops Lydeard, Somerset, but was to end up very derelict in one of the company's quarries at St Audries near Minehead, from where it was rescued for preservation in 1957.

Tasker's built wagons over a fifteen-year period from 1910 onwards, and in total around 120 were constructed. Competing against Fodens, Tasker's wagons never achieved high sales, the Foden design being generally regarded as a faster wagon.

One of the most successful of Tasker's designs was the 'Little Giant' tractor. Quite a number are in preservation, the oldest being class A1 no. 1296 *The Horse's Friend*, a 3 nhp single-cylinder slide-valve 3 ton engine built in 1902. Its name originates from its working days when it was used to help horses hauling heavy loads up steep hills. There are two other A1 class tractors surviving, together with many more examples of the B2 class 5 nhp design, the oldest of which was constructed in 1908. These are compound slide-valve engines. One of them, no. 1822 *Horatio*, was built in 1920 and used on the fairgrounds by Smarts of Warminster, hauling and providing power for a set of dodgems. In its final commercial years it was employed on timber haulage.

Tasker's built a few tractors specifically for showmen. One such was no. 1778 *Marshall Foch*, built in 1919 and supplied new to Theodore Frankham of Bristol, travelling mostly in the west country. It was scrapped as late as 1952.

Tasker's also designed a tandem road-roller, but only one was built. No. 1913 of 1924 was originally ordered by Kirkcudbright County Council but was not delivered for some reason. It stood at Tasker's works until 1931 when it was sold to A.E. Prior of Limehouse, London. It was eventually scrapped.

There are only six Tasker traction engines in preservation in the British Isles. No. 1352, an 'Economic' type 7 nhp single slide-valve engine, was completed in August 1905. It is seen here at the Great Dorset Steam Fair, a Hampshire County Council Museum Services exhibit.

This is Tasker B2 5 nhp compound slide-valve tractor no. 1599, built in 1914, pictured on display in the marquee erected for the Wallis & Steevens and Tasker's Exhibition at the 1992 Great Dorset Steam Fair. This engine is part of the Tasker collection belonging to Hampshire County Council Museum Services.

Many of the remaining engines built by W. Tasker & Sons Ltd belong to the Hampshire County Council Museum Services including 'Little Giant' B2 tractor no. 1726 *Blossom*, completed in April 1917. This is a compound slide-valve 5 nhp engine. Notice the highly polished brass maker's plate near the footplate.

Tasker's also built a small 3 nhp single-cylinder slide-valve tractor. These class A1 tractors were designed for one-man operation on light haulage work for market gardeners, furniture removers and the like. Three still remain in preservation. No. 1318, pictured here, was completed in August 1906 and supplied to E. Prosser of Bathurst, Kent, the engine being used for hauling coal from the railhead to Mr Prosser's large house. In the 1930s it was purchased by the Longhurst Estate and used on timber work.

Tasker 'Little Giant' 5 nhp tractor no. 1902 *St Amant* was completed in September 1925 and supplied new to E. Hicks of Tunbridge Wells, being used on brick haulage. In 1939 it returned to the Tasker works at Andover for conversion to a roller, in which form it worked until 1955. Since being purchased for preservation the engine has been restored to a tractor.

This Tasker 10 ton roller, works no. 1933, is a 'C' class single-cylinder slide-valve engine completed in April 1928 and sold to Watson & Haig Ltd of Andover. It is part of the Tasker collection in the ownership of Hampshire County Council Museum Services.

Tasker's was also involved in the steam wagon market. Only one example survives in the British Isles, the 5 ton tipping wagon no. 1915, built in 1924. This wagon was supplied to W.J. King of Bishops Lydeard, better known for its fleet of Foden wagons. The Tasker ended up derelict at King's Quarry, St Audries near Minehead, from where it was rescued in 1957. It has been superbly restored by its owners, Hampshire County Council Museum Services.

John I. Thorneycroft & Co. Ltd
Worting Road, Basingstoke

This well-known company was only involved with the production of steam-powered vehicles for a few years before turning their attention wholly to internal combustion units in the early 1900s. Its steam interests were transferred under licence to Duncan Stewart & Co. Ltd, Glasgow. Thorneycroft produced several designs for both the home and overseas markets. The oldest surviving vehicle is no. 1, a van built in 1896 at Chiswick. Its first public appearance was at the 1896 Crystal Palace Motor Show where it was the only industrial vehicle on display. Remarkable as it may seem today, no. 1 was driven from Chiswick all the way to Cardiff for the official opening of a dealership. Fortunately this historic vehicle survived, appearing at the 50th anniversary celebrations at Basingstoke in May 1946. It remained in the company's museum until 1972 when it went to Beaulieu Motor Museum where it stayed until 1983, after which it went on display at the Commercial Vehicle Museum, Leyland. In 1991, following boiler work, it was seen in action at Basingstoke.

Thorneycroft's achieved successful sales with several municipal operators. In 1897 no. 2 appeared. This was a tipper supplied to Chiswick UDC. It was followed in 1898 by an articulated vehicle capable of carrying a 5 ton load. Other designs included 2 ton steam tractors for use by the army in the South African campaign; these were regarded as a successful design. At the turn of the century Thorneycroft's supplied steam-powered buses to Burma, but how these fared one can only wonder.

There are two other Thorneycrofts in preservation. No. 115 of 1902, also preserved at the Commercial Vehicle Museum, is lettered County Borough of Bournemouth speed 5 mph! This wagon was to be seen in steam at the 1981 Expo at Peterborough. The other survivor, no. 39 of October 1900, is preserved at Boston with a dray type body lettered Phipps Brewery Ltd, Northampton. This is thought to have been added in preservation days.

Thorneycroft no. 1, a 1.5 ton twin-cylinder compound van, was built in 1896 at Chiswick in London, and later that year was exhibited at the Crystal Palace Motor Show. Construction of a new works at Worting Road in Basingstoke commenced two years later, but it was not many years before the company concentrated on internal combustion engine vehicles. In the early 1900s steam was transferred under licence to Duncan Stewart & Co. Ltd of Glasgow. No. 1 is pictured here in 1991 at the Thorneycroft rally at Basingstoke. It was in steam following recent boiler work.

Life must have been very difficult on the road for the drivers of these early wagons, with no protection against the weather conditions. Thorneycroft no. 115 was completed in March 1902. The lettering on the wagon reads 'County Borough of Bournemouth no. 4'. It also has a notice that reads 'maximum speed five miles per hour'.

There are only two Thorneycroft wagons in preservation in the British Isles. No. 39 was completed in October 1900. The lettering reads Phipps Brewery Ltd, Northampton, although this may have been added in preservation days. This interesting example has been preserved at Boston for many years.

Wallis & Steevens Ltd
North Hants Ironworks, Basingstoke

Steamrollers were an important part of this company's engine production, especially the very successful 'Advance' design, but it was also involved with many other types for both the home and overseas markets. A considerable number of engines have survived into preservation, including a large number of rollers, many of which were still working in the 1950s and 1960s. The company entered the competitive showmen's engines market just before the turn of the century. One example which was well known in its day was the heavily decorated 7 nhp *Royal John*, no. 2643, which was built in 1903 and worked for Henry Jennings of Devizes, Wiltshire. Sadly it has not survived.

Tractors were another important market for Wallis & Steevens. The oldest survivor is no. 2592, a 3 ton 3 nhp single-cylinder engine built in 1902. The company later introduced its 'oil bath' compound design, which had enclosed motion running in an oil bath; several examples built between 1907 and 1930 have survived. Many of the tractors constructed around the time of the First World War were requisitioned. One of these was no. 7482 a 4 nhp 'oil bath' compound, which was sent to do threshing work in Berkshire. In 1925 it was purchased by Goodey Bros of Twyford who used it for a short time to haul their set of gallopers. After a period on stone haulage it was laid up, eventually spending forty years in a scrapyard where the ravages of time and weather took their toll. When purchased for preservation it required extensive restoration. Two tractors at one time in preservation here have gone to new owners in Japan and the United States.

There is only one surviving Wallis & Steevens wagon in the British Isles. It is currently being restored. A 5 ton wagon, no. 7279, it was completed in April 1912 and supplied new to Pickfords Ltd, becoming fleet no. 104. After a very short period it passed into the ownership of J.W. Lance & Son of Lymington, hants, and during the following years it was to have four more owners before it was rescued for preservation in 1963. This wagon is now part of the Hampshire County Council Museum Services collection.

Wallis & Steevens built traction engines from 1877 in several designs including the well-known 'Expansion' type. The oldest survivor, a 7 nhp single-cylinder engine, was built in 1883. Happily, the last 'Expansion' type to be built, no. 8052 *East Lothian Star*, has survived. This 6 nhp single-cylinder engine was completed in December 1930, when the demand for traction engines had fallen to a low point. It was exhibited at Belfast show in 1936.

The company built a great many road-rollers. The first, an 'Expansion' type, was completed in 1890 but this particular engine has not survived. No. 2357, completed in October 1896, is the oldest survivor by four years of the company's early rollers which included both single-cylinder and compound designs. In 1923 the first of the revolutionary and popular 'Advance' rollers made its public appearance. Designed for the newer road surfaces with high-pressure cylinders and piston valves, these rollers were to become a familiar sight on our highways over the years. Luckily the prototype is in preservation: no. 7773 of July 1923, a 4 nhp 6 ton engine. Production continued until 1939, with engines of 6, 8 and 10 ton weights. There are nearly eighty examples in preservation in Britain.

In 1925 the 'Simplicity' roller appeared. Designed principally for the overseas market, this design incorporated an inclined stayless boiler barrel with a tubular firebox, which allowed for low cost and easy maintenance. Many rollers of this design were actually to find themselves working in the British Isles rather than being exported. The prototype, no. 7832, was supplied to E. Parry & Co., Putney, later passing into the ownership of the well-known highways contractors W. & J. Glossop. In all six examples are in preservation.

Wallis & Steevens produced a reliable general purpose traction engine known as the 'Expansion' type. No. 7666 *Wheatsheaf* is a good example. This 7 nhp single-cylinder slide-valve engine was completed in March 1919 for the War Department, but as the war had already finished when it was completed, it soon passed into private ownership working in Kent. It ended up derelict, in this case being abandoned for thirty-five years before being rescued.

Restoration of a derelict engine is a daunting prospect. This is Wallis & Steevens 8 nhp traction no. 2959, built in 1907 and supplied new to Wm A. Cary of Steeple Ashton, Wiltshire. It ended its working days at Bulmer in Essex. It was sold in 1957 to Mr Philp, and was one of the items sold at the Philp auction sale in 1995, after many years of exposure to the elements.

This traction engine is typical of the thousands of single-cylinder engines built by the leading companies. It is 5 nhp Wallis & Steevens no. 7159 *Shamrock Mist*, completed in October 1910. This picture was taken at Pickering.

Over the years the early history of some engines became lost in the mist of time, as happened with this 3 nhp Wallis & Steevens tractor, works number unknown. It is thought to have been built in around 1904. It is known to have worked at one stage at Warner's Brick & Tile Works, Knowle Hill near Reading. *Goliath* has been on the rally scene for many years.

This fine example of the Wallis & Steevens 'oil bath' compound slide-valve tractor is works no. 7802, completed in November 1924. During its working life it was owned by James Penfold of Arundel, Sussex, and used in the southern counties. Only three tractors built after this one have survived in the British Isles. Production at the works from this time on was mostly concentrated on road-rollers of the 'Advance' design.

This 4 nhp 'oil bath' Wallis & Steevens tractor, no. 7482 *Royal Star*, was completed in December 1914 and promptly requisitioned by the War Office, who sent it for threshing work to Hollands of Chaddleworth, Berkshire, its second agricultural owner. It was purchased in 1925 by Goodey Brothers of Twyford and used to haul their gallopers and other fairground equipment. This was short-lived, the tractor soon finding itself on stone haulage at Twyford. It was laid aside for forty years, eventually becoming derelict.

Only one Wallis & Steevens wagon still survives in the British Isles. This is 5 ton wagon no. 7279, completed at Basingstoke in April 1912. It was supplied new to Pickfords, becoming fleet no. 104. Within a short time it was sold to J.W. Lance of Lymington, Hants, and had four other owners before it was rescued. The wagon is seen here at Dorset in the early stages of restoration.

The most successful of the Wallis & Steevens roller designs was the 'Advance', a large number of which were constructed. Many have survived into preservation. This fine example is no. 7784, a 6 ton two-speed model built in 1923. In its later years it was owned by Wirksworth Quarries.

Only fifteen Wallis & Steevens 'Simplicity' 3 ton rollers were built, and they were principally intended for export to the Far East. In spite of this more remained in Britain than went overseas. These cheap and easy to maintain engines have a tubular firebox within the inclined boiler barrel. Although there are six examples in preservation they are not often seen on the rally field. No. 7981 was completed in April 1929 and supplied the following year to Thomas C. White of Guildford, Surrey.

Yorkshire Patent Steam Wagon Co.
Pepper Road, Leeds

The few surviving very early steam wagons are particularly interesting. Doubtless in their day they offered far from ideal working conditions with little more than a wooden bench seat and the driver and his mate exposed to everything the elements – and the engine – could throw at them. They ran on solid wheels, some of a cart-type construction. One of the earliest surviving wagons is Yorkshire's no. 117, easily recognizable with its transversely mounted boiler. This 2 ton wagon was completed in September 1905.

Four other wagons survive, one of which is not complete. No. 652, built in 1914 and a 6 ton wagon, no. 940, class WA, built in May 1917 are both complete. The restoration of the latter is a remarkable piece of engineering work, as at one time the wagon had been cut into pieces and was regarded as a hopeless case. However, advances in engineering practice enabled it to be carefully and painstakingly restored. This wagon was supplied new to Clayton & Son Engineers of Leeds who kept it for just two years before selling it on to Robinson & Birdsells Ltd in the Hunslet district of Leeds. Here it was used for scrap metal haulage until 1931 when it was laid aside, having been replaced by a more modern vehicle. As time passed it became buried in scrap and, perhaps rather surprisingly, survived the scrap metal drive during the Second World War. It was discovered in 1961 and since restoration it has taken part in many events including the London to Brighton run.

Yorkshire WG class no. 2108 is of very different appearance. When built it was listed as a semi-arctic type and was supplied to Leeds Council Electricity Department originally as no. 2128. Conversion to the present type with shaft drive and pneumatic tyres took place in 1936. Eventually the wagon was scrapped, ending up at Robinson & Birdsells at Hunslet from where it was rescued and completed restored. Currently preserved in Somerset it can, on occasions, be seen at the Great Dorset Steam Fair resplendent in red livery and easily distinguishable from the Sentinels by its flat front end.

The final Yorkshire survivor is a tractor unit from an articulated wagon originally preserved in Yorkshire as part of the Gisburn collection. It was sold some years ago and moved south. This tractor was built in 1927 and supplied with the unit to Leeds Electricity Department. It was later rebuilt as a ballast tractor. In due course it became derelict and fortunately was rescued for preservation.

At one time Yorkshire's had a thriving wagon market throughout the British Isles and overseas. One important home customer was Newcastle upon Tyne Corporation which operated a fleet of 3.5 ton wagons for waste collection. Yorkshire wagons were available in a range of bodies, including box types, tankers etc. They also supplied gully emptiers to several corporations, including Reigate, Rochdale and the Metropolitan Borough of Fulham.

Several other designs also appeared over the years, such as a roadrail tractor unit and a chain-driven tractor, examples of which were supplied to the South African Railways and Harbour Board. Later catalogues over the years appeared under the name 'The Yorkshire Commercial Motor Co.'

The Yorkshire wagons with their transversely mounted boilers are instantly recognizable but sadly only a small number have survived into preservation. No. 940 is a WA class 3 ton example built in 1917 and supplied new to Clayton Son & Co., Engineers in Leeds. It did not remain with them for long, passing into the ownership of Robinson & Birdsells Ltd of Hunslet who used it for scrap metal haulage until 1931, before it was laid aside. It is remarkable that it is still with us at all as in 1961 it was cut into pieces, and at the time was regarded as unrestorable.

The Yorkshire Patent Steam Wagon Co. built this 6 nhp 6 ton example, works no. 652, in 1914. The transversely mounted boiler is prominent. It is pictured here on display at the special wagon exhibition at the 1995 Great Dorset Steam Fair.

This class WG Yorkshire was originally built as works no. 2118, as an articulated unit for Leeds Electricity Department in 1927. It was later rebuilt as a ballast tractor and was eventually to end up derelict.